Editor:
Susan Leslie DuBois

Layout and Design:
Lynn Oliver, Graphic Designer
lynnoliver.com

Photography:
Susan Leslie DuBois
Rick Guidotti, Positive Exposure
Michelle O'Connor
Lynn Oliver
Christina Sandberg, Sandberg Photography
Mashawna Thompson
Linda Wood
KJ Sikkema Photography
and, the Bergman Family

First edition: June 2008
Second printing: January 2011
Third printing: December 2015

Published by:
The National Organization for Albinism and Hypopigmentation (NOAH)
PO Box 959
East Hampstead, NH 03826

ISBN 978-0-615-20927-2

Library of Congress Control Number
2008928496

Printed in the U.S. by:
Wharf Industries Printing, Inc.
3 Lexington Road, Unit 2
Windham, NH 03087

Third edition printing made possible with contributions from: Lighthouse for the Blind - St. Louis

Raising a Child with Albinism

A Guide to the Early Years

By the **National Organization for Albinism and Hypopigmentation**

About NOAH

The **National Organization for Albinism and Hypopigmentation** (NOAH) was founded in 1982 to offer information and support to individuals with albinism, their families and the many professionals who work with them. NOAH's mission is to promote public acceptance and understanding of albinism and related conditions, and to encourage research that will lead to improved diagnosis and management of albinism. NOAH is operated by its members on a volunteer basis and is funded primarily by dues and contributions.

NOAH also seeks to create a community of caring people to improve the lives of those with albinism around the world. The group sponsors workshops and conferences on albinism, publishes a quarterly newsletter called *Albinism InSight*, and publishes information bulletins on topics specific to living with albinism. NOAH maintains a network of local chapters and contact people, and operates a website that has information about albinism and bulletin boards where people can share experiences.

For more information about NOAH, or to join and help support its mission, visit the website at **www.albinism.org**, or send an e-mail to **info@ albinism.org**.

Table of Contents

Welcome

When our son was diagnosed with albinism shortly after his birth in 2000, we were overwhelmed. Our world was filled with uncertainty; there were differing opinions from medical specialists, many unfamiliar acronyms and genetic questions. One doctor said he would be blind and another told us "he *should* lead a normal life." I have often told people that if I could have seen a picture of a child with albinism riding a bicycle – I would have been a lot calmer.

Just knowing that he would be able to do something so ordinary would have been a great comfort. Instead, I spent the first five months of Nick's life indoors with the shades drawn, wondering if he would ever see airplanes or the moon.

Back then, the NOAH online community was still new, and not a significant amount of information was available about what to expect as our son grew. Getting accurate information from doctors was even more difficult.

By the time our second child, Katy, was born with albinism in 2002, things had begun to change. Today, the NOAH website continues to be a great resource,

Photo courtesy of Susan Leslie DuBois

and the online community has become a powerful tool for information and assistance. We also have in place the NOAH Rapid Responder program to put parents in immediate touch with others who can answer questions and help give peace of mind.

Even with these advances, too many new parents are still overwhelmed. My hope is that this book will teach you that your kids will play, run, paint and read – just like all of the other kids. My children can see the stars, the moon and fish in the water. They constantly amaze me, and I learn from them every day.

Acknowledgements

This book is truly a collaborative effort, and would not have been possible without the combined talents of many dedicated people. It has taken more than three years, two NOAH conferences, hundreds of e-mails and many conference calls. It has gone through several drafts and countless earnest conversations with eager participants. It would be impossible for me to convey the depth of my gratitude to all of the people who have helped bring this to fruition. At the risk of leaving someone out, and with the knowledge that many others touched this book with their encouragement, I offer appreciation, special thanks and acknowledgements to the following people:

Kim Avila, COMS and teacher of students with visual impairments, who also has albinism, for her overall guidance and her hard work on all of the sections involving stimulating vision, adaptive devices, and the role of service providers; Jeannine Stearns for providing a wealth of knowledge and experience, and for contributing to the sections on social skills and self-esteem; and Dr. Rick Thompson, OD, an optometrist and a parent of a child with albinism, for his contributions on defining albinism, the impact on the structure of the eye and vision, the medical profession and treatment options.

Chris Kramer for writing about adoption; Donna Appell for her contributions on Hermansky-Pudlak Syndrome; Matt Bailey for his perspective on how people with albinism see; Brendan Nolan and Kelly Povilaitis for their personal essay and work on the resource section; Margaret McEvoy for her contribution to the section on self-esteem; Ja-Nae Epps, Saundra Sanders and Garcia Lee for working on the section regarding people of color with albinism; Kelsey Thompson and John Schmit for writing about social issues; Margaret Mary Campbell for writing about early reading strategies; Randi Ostrove for her contribution on early childhood education; Anna Swenson, Teacher of Students with Visual Impairments, for her contributions to the vision sections; Vicky Vaught for her work on ocular albinism and early intervention services; and Sue Dalton, Rita Jackson and Kelly Hoynoski for their support and help.

Kathy Goldgeier for editing the manuscript, and Lynn Oliver for providing the book's layout and graphic design. Rick Guidotti from Positive Exposure and Linda Wood, a parent of a child with albinism, for providing the beautiful images that enhance the book. Also, thanks to Dan Lee, who coordinated the printing of the book. And finally, to the parents of children with albinism and the adults with albinism whose personal anecdotes are scattered throughout the book – *thank you for sharing your stories*.

The contributing authors have drawn on their own experience, along with that of many other parents, educators, medical professionals and experts in the albinism community. Any factual information that is not attributed to an individual or an organization is taken from the NOAH website. The authors have attempted to provide

accurate information in a neutral manner, and regret any errors or omissions.

I would also like to thank the collegiate sorority **Delta Gamma** for the generous *"Service for Sight"* grant. Delta Gamma was founded in 1873 in Oxford, Mississippi, and has dedicated itself to making a positive impact in the lives of people who are blind or visually impaired. Delta Gamma supports a variety of vision-related organizations, including NOAH.

This book would not have been possible without the generous support and assistance from NOAH, and all of the wonderful people who serve it, with particular thanks for the grant from the Northern Illinois Chapter. I offer sincere appreciation to my friends at NOAH and to the organization itself for their support, encouragement and invaluable contributions to both the content and execution of this project. Special thanks to **Mike McGowan** for guiding the project to completion, and to **Lori Aubrey** for her invaluable assistance.

Most important, thanks to my family, **Doug**, **Nick** and **Katy**, for wholeheartedly supporting my effort to share our own experiences and newfound knowledge with other families like ours.

Susan Leslie DuBois
Parent and principal author
April 2008

Foreword

Being a parent is perhaps life's greatest challenge. Having a child with albinism adds a unique component to the awesome responsibilities of parenthood. A stark reality that parents of children with albinism encounter almost immediately upon receiving a diagnosis is that there are few authoritative resources immediately available to inform and guide them.

In Philadelphia, in 1982, a small group of individuals pledged themselves to forming an organization dedicated to providing information and support to the albinism community. Since then NOAH, inspired by the vision, talent and perseverance of the founders, and fueled by the selfless dedication of many volunteers, has worked to fill the information void. By bringing people together and compiling and disseminating information about albinism, NOAH enlightens and sustains those who live with the condition.

This book marks a significant accomplishment for NOAH and the albinism community. It provides the parents of young children with albinism a concise resource to address the unique journey on which they find themselves.

With sincere thanks to the principal author, Susan Leslie DuBois, all those who contributed their insight, wisdom and knowledge, and to the NOAH benefactors who made this project possible, it is my honor and privilege to present this important volume.

Mike McGowan
adult with albinism
President of NOAH
February 2008

Introduction

If you are reading this book, chances are good that you are a new parent of a child with albinism. Congratulations! Your journey may be different than you expected, but it will be rewarding and joyful. The first, and most important, message to take from this book is: **Relax. Really.**

Your child will see more, do more and accomplish more than you think, and you will learn that albinism is only a small part of the person he or she will become. It may seem difficult to enjoy your child without worrying about what the future will bring, but we hope this book will help you do just that.

The goal of this book is to provide parents and caregivers with a resource guide for raising a child with albinism in the early years. We have tried to explain what albinism is (and isn't); to provide suggestions for stimulating vision and for obtaining appropriate services; to explain the technology and medical terms you will encounter; and also to help you to see your child first and the albinism second. The photographs of children with albinism in the book are included to show you beautiful, talented and accomplished children – who happen to have albinism.

The book focuses on the development of a child with albinism from birth to first grade. Other publications deal with the more specific educational and social issues that arise in later adolescent years. Please visit the NOAH website at **www.albinism.org** for more information.

This book is not intended to replace the assistance and advice of professionals. We urge you to seek competent medical advice and appropriate early intervention services – discussed at length in the following pages. Our goal here is to offer you the tools to be an effective advocate for your child and to help your child develop the necessary skills to thrive.

Chapter 1

Welcoming a Child with Albinism into Your Life

Parenting a child with albinism may be no more difficult than raising any other child, but there are specific issues that are unique to this experience. The goal of this book is to give you clear and neutral information about raising a child with albinism in the early years and providing an environment in which your child will thrive.

This chapter starts at the beginning and will help you deal with the diagnosis and explain it to your family. It also discusses some of the ways you can start to adapt your child's physical environment to best meet his individual needs.

Adjusting to the News

Learning that your child has a genetic condition can be a difficult experience. Each of us has had to grapple with the fear of the unknown and the worry that accompanies the knowledge that our child has a health condition. Albinism is rare, so parents are often faced with a lack of information and sensitivity from the medical profession.

Your child may have been diagnosed with albinism right away, because he was born with white hair, or perhaps your doctor noticed the differences apparent in your baby's eyes. Or you may have consulted your pediatrician because you were surprised to see the involuntary eye movement called nystagmus that appears at about ten weeks of age.

Maybe you are African-American or Asian and were immediately aware of a significant difference in your baby's skin color. Some children are not diagnosed until they are older, but most families learn their child's preliminary diagnosis within the first year.

Each family has a different story to tell about how they received their diagnosis. Your experience may have been positive, or you may have been given little or no information about the realities of living with albinism. Unfortunately, some families receive misinformation, but others are lucky to encounter well-informed doctors or medical staff right from the start.

Whether your child is four days old or four months old, the first few days after the diagnosis can be the most difficult. It is entirely normal to feel bewildered, sad or angry when you learn that your child has a genetic disorder. Some people accept the information relatively quickly and move right along in their parenting. Others struggle with the diagnosis, and go through the classic stages of grief. It's OK to cry. And you shouldn't feel guilty if you are scared or sad. Many new parents feel that way early on, and struggle with acceptance. There is no "right" way to cope with something as significant as your child's health, and each person must find his or her own path.

Allow yourself time to adjust to the diagnosis of albinism. Your first reaction may be to read as much as possible about albinism, to spend hours on the National Organization for Albinism and Hypopigmentation website (**www.albinism.org**), and to seek the opinion of medical specialists in an attempt to "fix" or "treat" the condition. Many parents feel a sense of urgency about treatment options in the early stages. These are all very normal reactions, but it is important to maintain a balanced perspective.

Try not to spend the first few precious months of your child's life captive to fears of the unknown. You may worry about all sorts of things: What can he see? Will he drive? Will he have friends? Will he be teased? It is normal to be concerned about all that, but there is really nothing you can do during your child's infancy to address those issues. Newborn babies have very limited vision anyway, and they certainly can't drive or make friends. While there are some important things you can do to help

"My wife Kelly and I received the news that our son, Connor, had albinism when he was twelve hours old. We didn't know anyone with this condition, so we were left looking at each other wondering how this would impact our son. We still had no idea that his vision would in any way be affected. We wanted the best for our son, and now we were left with an empty feeling as if he had been shortchanged.

What we wanted next was information. I'm not sure if we were just lucky, but we seemed to run into so many good people who did so much to help us understand his condition, starting with the hospital pediatrician who was sharp enough to catch a condition not seen very often. The following day we met with a geneticist who was called in to give us the specifics. After a night of worry it was great to hear someone explain to us what albinism was. The doctor was excellent, incredibly thorough, deliberately patient and impressively kind. He was the springboard of our understanding Connor's condition.

The next step in the process is coming to terms with the problems our son will encounter throughout his life. In these situations there seems to be a tendency to think first of the worst. "He will be blind," we thought, looking at his tightly closed eyes in the NICU.

We worried about how he would be treated in school. "Will he be teased? Will he be picked on? We want him to have friends. We want him to be a part of things." People would walk by and comment on his white hair. "Look at the towhead," was a common refrain. This just made us scream inside - we got so angry that people didn't understand. It was not their fault. We didn't get it at first either. So, over time, we went through the worst-case scenarios in our heads, and expelled the demons.

Every time we held Connor, I could feel my heart getting lighter. He would wrap his little hands around my finger, and I would melt right there. Funny how such an instinctual function holds such meaning in the minds of parents. We touched his wisps of white hair and wondered if ever there could be a child more incredible. In those moments we forgot about albinism, and we saw only our son. As the days went on, we began to again link the two, but this time we saw albinism as something unique. In order to completely embrace our son, we had to embrace all. Albinism is a part of him and will help define him for the rest of his life. My wife and I will have the unique and incredible role of guiding his development as the world opens up to him.

Brendan Nolan"
Royal Oak, MI
parent of a child with albinism

your child (which we will discuss in great detail), albinism is a largely static condition, and you won't hurt your child by taking some time to absorb this shift in your life.

You may hear from people that you should be grateful that your child's health issues are not more serious. Don't feel the need to respond or to defend your feelings to anyone. It is difficult to adequately explain to people both how sad you may be that your child has a genetic condition and how thrilled you are by his seeming perfection. Talk to your spouse or partner about the impact of albinism in his or her life, too. You will both experience a change in perspective and expectations as parents. However, parenthood will always be full of challenges and surprises – yours just may be more apparent.

Feelings of sadness can be a normal part of the coping experience for a new parent dealing with the challenges of albinism. Don't berate yourself for having sad moments, or even for crying at unexpected times. Bringing a new baby into your family can be a stressful event, whether or not your baby has pigment. However, if either you or your spouse is experiencing a prolonged feeling of melancholy, please consult a medical professional. You may have a mild form of depression, or a case of post partum depression.

"The reality is that there is no normal… there are only varying shades of different." *–Beth Wiggs*

Redefining Normal

The healthiest step you can take right now in your journey as a parent is to begin to change your perspective. Because most children with albinism have low vision, this may mean learning to connect with your baby without eye contact in those first few months. It may mean accepting that it will be normal for your child to always wear a hat and sunglasses on sunny days, and to hold a book a few inches from his face when he reads. It will be normal for you to use lots of descriptive language to explain something visual to your child. It will be normal for him to have a tougher time with visual tasks or hobbies. Working through the difficulties with patience and humor will help your child develop the skills he'll need as an adult.

Your child's visual behavior may differ from that of other children, and you will have to learn to interpret it. When your baby becomes fussy, you will learn to consider causes related to his albinism. For example, his sensitivity to bright sunlight creeping in through the shade may be the cause of his discomfort. Increased eye movement will tell you that he might be tired, and increased squinting will tell you the room is too bright. A persistent head tilt or crossing of his eyes may alert you to an issue to discuss with your doctor.

Still, it is important to remember that your child has never known anything different. His vision is normal for him, and will improve somewhat as he gets older. Your child may not even understand that he sees differently than others until you explain it to him. However, even as you are readjusting your perspective, remember that your child can and should participate with typically-developing children in everyday activities such as play groups and child-centered community classes. These activities will help your child develop physically, cognitively and socially, and will also provide others with learning experiences about people with albinism and visual impairments.

Don't imagine a world without beach vacations or baseball in the backyard – you will have all of that, if you want it. Children with albinism play sports, ride bicycles and love to swim. In short, they are just like all little kids. They just need extra protection outdoors and some modifications to accommodate for their low vision and light sensitivity. With the right kind of sun protection, your child will enjoy the outdoors as much as any other kid. It may be difficult to imagine it now, but in a few short years, your child will be running around a park or playground with glee.

> I cannot tell you how important it is to teach your child that there is nothing wrong with him and that he can accomplish almost anything in life if he has the right attitude and accommodations. Teaching self-awareness and creativity and a "can do" attitude is the most significant thing you can do for your child. Make him do chores and treat him like a NORMAL child who has specific limitations that need accommodation. The reality is that there is no normal… there are only varying shades of different.
>
> Beth Wiggs
> Arlington, TX
> adult with albinism

Photo courtesy of Positive Exposure, Rick Guidotti

Dealing with the Reaction of Family and Friends

You may also be concerned about how to tell your family that your child has albinism. Telling your family about your child's diagnosis may prompt a wide range of reactions. Some family members may be entirely supportive, while others are confused or dismissive of the condition. Whichever the scenario, the way you frame the issue will have an impact on how they handle the information. It is important to be open and honest with your family about albinism, so they learn to accept and deal with it. Using clear, neutral language to teach your family and friends the basics about albinism is important because it sets the stage for acceptance of your child.

Sometimes parents and grandparents experience feelings of guilt, because a genetic condition must be "passed down." While these feelings are normal and understandable, they are unproductive and expend energy on something that cannot be altered. Try to avoid discussions about where in the family it came from, and focus on education and acceptance. Remind your family that in most cases, albinism is passed down from both sides of the family, and an estimated one in seventy people carry some form of albinism in their genetic makeup. If possible, take family members to the doctor's office with you, so they can ask questions and understand the diagnosis.

You may also choose to help your family better understand and accept albinism by inviting them to NOAH events, encouraging them to explore the NOAH website, and most importantly, inviting them to spend time with your child. Many grandparents and other family members attend the bi-annual NOAH conferences, which is a wonderful place to meet accomplished people with albinism. The conferences also have workshops for family members and provide a safe place to ask lots of questions. In addition, NOAH sponsors several family activities throughout the year.

Adoption and Albinism

Most parents have no idea they are going to have a child with albinism until the child is born. Adoption is a little different, especially international adoption. Parents who adopt a child with albinism have more information when they begin the process – but not always a lot more. Often, you are shown a photo and given few details about the child. Then you have to make a decision about whether or not this child would be a good "fit" with your particular family. You may be completely unfamiliar with albinism, you may have negative preconceptions about albinism, or you may have a friend or family member with albinism. All of that influences your decision. Often, you only have a few days to do some quick research, maybe contact other parents who have adopted a similar child, and discuss the issue with friends and family.

Then you say yes. Congratulations! You are going to be a parent of an amazing child.

Nonetheless, you may also be asked why you adopted a child with albinism instead of a "normal" one or why the child was abandoned by his birth parents. The answers will vary, but many cultures have a negative view of albinism. In China, for instance, albinism is often viewed as a curse. People with albinism are excluded from many jobs, have difficulty finding someone to marry and are considered unlucky. You may be questioned by the adoption community as well because some well-meaning people do not consider a child with albinism to be a true "native" of his country of origin. Of course, he is just as "native" as any other child adopted from that country. Your own factual understanding of these issues will allow you to give straightforward answers to these questions.

As he gets older, a child who comes to you through an international adoption will not only have to deal with possible vision and skin issues, but will also find himself explaining that he was not born in this country. Older adopted children may have the added task of learning a new language. The key to helping your toddler or school-age child is to be his advocate in school by educating yourself about the laws that provide assistance for special needs children and then actively participating in developing a program that works best for your child.

You may also choose to get involved in the local adoption community and educate other parents. Let them see that your child can run,

play, be goofy, throw tantrums and act just like every other child on the planet. If you are adopting from an Asian country, there is an excellent Internet chat group called BaiChina listed in the Resource section that can offer support and answer questions throughout your journey into parenthood.

Your extended family will also require continued education. You may need to sit down and explain to them why you are adopting this particular child. If they don't understand immediately, give them some time. Refer them to NOAH, remind them of your child's vision and skincare needs when they are together, and let them see your child in action. Then you're likely to hear them say, "He doesn't act like he has a visual impairment!" Once your extended family comes to know and understand your child, they will fall in love with him too.

Public Reaction and Questions

Every parent of a child with albinism will hear questions and comments and notice the stares. It is important to remember that your child will develop a large part of his attitude about albinism from the way you handle these situations. When you are asked (for the hundredth time), "Where did he get that white hair?" your child will pick up on your reaction, so do your best not to be annoyed or embarrassed. Although it is difficult when dealing with a rude stranger, remaining calm and neutral when discussing albinism in front of your child is an important step in helping him develop a healthy attitude about it.

Every family will develop its own set of responses to the questions and the inevitable comments. You may view these opportunities as "teachable moments" – or you may not. You will not always feel like offering a complete explanation of albinism and how it affects your family and your child. Answer questions when you want to, but do not feel obligated to educate everyone who asks about albinism. You may want to consider how often a person is likely to encounter your child, and let that guide your decision about how much information to share. Developing some handy one-line replies will help too.

In addition, NOAH has developed a small, informational card you can use to help impart information. On the front is a photo of people with albinism. On the back is a short explanation of albinism, with an invitation to find out more on the NOAH website. These cards can be very handy for those times when people are staring or asking questions and you just don't feel like engaging with them. Handing one of these cards to a rude person and quietly walking away can help you feel better and also educate that person. You can find out more about the card at the NOAH website, **www.albinism.org**.

You may also feel awkward when you encounter someone else with albinism. Do you go up to him or not? What do you say if you do? Again, each situation must be judged individually. If you can talk privately, that may be easier than if you are in a crowded public area. You might introduce yourself and explain your connection with albinism and then ask if the person has been diagnosed also, or has ever heard of NOAH. However, don't be offended if a parent or an adult with albinism doesn't feel like talking with you, since he or she may be wary from other interactions with less well-informed strangers.

As your child approaches school age, consider encouraging him to answer questions about albinism in his own words. After all, he will be answering these questions on his own soon enough. Talking about how to respond to these situations will give your child an opportunity to ask questions himself, and to become more comfortable handling them on his own. One four-year-old shocked his parents with his forthrightness when he marched up to the other kids on his new soccer team, introduced himself first by his first name, and then told them, "I have nystagmus (the involuntary eye movement common with albinism)." No one asked him anything about it after that!

Taking the First Steps

While it is important just to relax and enjoy your child, there are a few things you can do early in his life to help. Since you are reading this book, someone has taken the most important first step and contacted NOAH. The connections you make through NOAH and the resources available should provide you with most of the help you will need. However, there are a few practical steps you can take in the early months that will make life easier for you and your child. Several of these topics are discussed at length in the following chapters, but these tips will get you started in the right direction.

Establish Contacts

After stocking up on baby-size hats and sunglasses, we strongly encourage you to take advantage of NOAH's Rapid Responder program. The program matches new parents with other parents in the same geographic region who can begin to answer your questions and try to help you get the information you need. In addition, they can be a great resource for building a community and meeting other families in your area. These experienced parents of children with albinism can be very helpful as you sort through your feelings and continue to ponder the questions you undoubtedly have.

To be matched with a parent in your area, call NOAH toll-free at 1-800-473-2310 and ask about the Rapid Responder program.

Another important step is to develop a relationship with a pediatrician you trust – not necessarily one experienced in albinism (which is unlikely anyway), but one who is sensitive and willing to give you good referrals. If possible, look for a "developmental pediatrician" who has experience with children who exhibit developmental delays. This is the medical professional that will help you closely monitor your child's progress, and will know when and if there is cause for concern. While developmental delays can occur for a variety of reasons, your pediatrician is in the best position to determine the necessary steps to help your child flourish.

Finally, it is very important for you to contact your county or state social service office to enroll your child in Early Intervention Services. Even if your child does not need any specific help right now, it is still important to be in contact with the appropriate agencies in case the need arises. The National Dissemination Center for Children with Disabilities (NICHCY) compiles disability-related resources for each state. Please see their website at **www.nichcy.org/states.htm** for assistance locating help in your state. Early Intervention Services are discussed more thoroughly in Chapter 8.

Modify Your Environment

There are simple ways to modify your home to accommodate your child's special needs with regard to glare, strong light sources, and vision development. Any area where there is intense direct sunlight may need to be draped or shaded, or you may want to position your child facing away from mid-day, direct sunlight. For example, placing the highchair in front of a kitchen window may make your child uncomfortable because he has to look into the bright light. It is best to keep light sources behind your child.

Fluorescent lights may be harder on the eyes than incandescent or other types of bulbs. Experiment with different wattage and types of bulbs to see if one is more comfortable for your child. Also, consider installing dimmer switches on your lights. They are available at home improvement stores, and are an easy, inexpensive way to subdue powerful or harsh lighting. Strategic placement of throw rugs can reduce glare on shiny, light-reflecting floors, and placemats on light-colored tables and surfaces can reduce glare. Dark contact paper on a white highchair tray can reduce glare at mealtimes, and shades or tinting for car windows can make your child much more comfortable while traveling. For young children, make sure the television or computer is not in front of a window, or shield it from glare, if possible. Enlarge the font and cursor on your home computer.

As your child gets older and begins to explore his environment, place colored tape along the edge of stairs or anywhere there is a change in grade. This will help your child learn to safely navigate his environment by giving him a clue as to when to step down. Many children will stop and check the grade change with their hand or foot when they come to a different colored floor surface, such as the threshold between a carpeted and tiled floor. These precautions are usually only necessary for a short time, while your child gets used to the environment. These measures are also applicable to schools and other places where your child may spend time.

Photo courtesy of Positive Exposure, Rick Guidotti

Stimulate Vision

It is important to consider the visual interest of your child's immediate surroundings, particularly in areas of the house and car where your child will spend a lot of time. You can let the three B's be your guide: **"Big, Bold and Bright."** Babies in general (and babies with albinism in particular) see high contrast, simple, large patterns best. Consider:

- Installing a ceiling fan with dark blades if you have light ceilings, because babies spend lots of time lying down.
- Buying toys, mobiles, or other items that are black and white or primary colors in high contrast, with large shapes or patterns. These are good for the crib, the wall next to the changing table, or other spots in the house where your infant will normally lie or sit.
- Placing a play blanket with a large, bold contrast pattern on the back of the passenger seat in the car so your baby faces it from his car seat, or using the blanket for tummy time.
- Offering a safe child's mirror to help teach early responses to facial expressions.
- Dressing yourself in clothing that is visually interesting – wear patterned or printed shirts in bold colors instead of solid colors or pastel prints and wear more vivid shades of nail polish and face makeup.

You will find more discussion of these tips throughout the book.

Chapter 2

What is Albinism?

This chapter offers a brief explanation of albinism that is intended to answer most of your basic questions about the condition. For more detailed information, ask your doctor or consult the NOAH website.

Albinism is a genetic condition most often characterized by a lack of pigment in a person's hair, eyes and skin. It is caused by inheriting a recessive gene from each parent, and occurs in approximately one in every 17,000 persons in the United States. While the condition is quite rare, one in seventy persons actually carries a recessive gene for a type of albinism. Two people who both have the recessive gene have a one in four chance that their child will have albinism. There are several different types of albinism, each with different characteristics. The most common forms are discussed below.

Oculocutaneous Albinism (OCA)

Oculocutaneous albinism (OCA) is the most common form of albinism, and exists in many different forms. OCA1 is caused by a genetic mutation involving the enzyme tyrosinase, which converts tyrosine into melanin. The first is referred to as OCA1a, and is sometimes called "complete albinism." It is characterized by the body's inability to change the amino acid tyrosine into melanin. People with OCA1a have no pigment, and have white hair, white skin and light blue, gray or violet eyes.

The second variation is OCA1b, in which people develop some level of tyrosinase activity and detectable amounts of pigment, and can even tan slightly. The amount of pigment varies in different people, but most doctors agree that people with OCA1b have some observable pigment by the age of 2. If your child shows no signs of any freckling or darkening of his hair or eyelashes by the age of 2, she most likely has OCA1a.

OCA2 is the most common form of albinism, and results from a mutation of a completely different gene that governs another enzyme for melanin production. People with OCA2 generally have slightly more pigment, and may have better vision that people with OCA1. There is no definitive way to tell whether your child has OCA1b or OCA2 without a genetic test, but the more pigment your child has and the better her vision, the more likely it is she has OCA2.

Ocular Albinism (OA)

The term "ocular albinism" describes an inherited condition that differs from OCA in that the eyes lack melanin pigment, but the skin and hair show normal or near-normal coloration. With ocular albinism, the color of the iris of the eye may vary from blue to green or even to brown, and sometimes darkens with age. However, the light shines back through the eye upon examination, since very little pigment is present in the retina.

The lack of pigment in the eye causes the same kinds of vision problems associated with other forms of albinism. In most cases, ocular albinism is X-linked, meaning the gene that causes it lies on the X chromosome. X-linked ocular albinism occurs almost exclusively in males. It is passed from mothers who carry the gene to their sons. A mother who carries the gene for ocular albinism has a one in two chance of passing it to her son, which would give the son ocular albinism. Mothers who carry the gene may have mottled pigmentation in the back of their eyes, but do not have the full syndrome of ocular albinism. An ophthalmologist may be able to identify this mottling in about 50 percent of cases. The only major difference between OCA and OA is x-linked inheritance. A boy with OA who has daughters will give each daughter a copy of his OA gene on his x chromosome, and each of his daughters will carry his OA gene. However, a boy with OA cannot pass OA to any son, because his son will not receive a copy of his x chromosome with OA.

In the past, it was thought there was another type of ocular albinism which was carried by both parents and which could be inherited by both boys and girls. It was called autosomal recessive ocular albinism or AROA. Many people with albinism have received this diagnosis in the past, and some practitioners continue to use it. However, newer research suggests that autosomal recessive ocular albinism is a variant of oculocutaneous albinism. Please see the NOAH information bulletin, available on the website, for more specific information.

> " I have two sons, but until my second son was born with OA, I had no idea I carried the gene for ocular albinism. An optometrist told me when I was younger that I had "albino spots" in my retina, but thankfully, he did not tell me what that meant. Had he told me, I might have opted against raising a family due to ignorance about albinism. Instead, I have been blessed with two sons, one with albinism and one without, both intelligent, both fully competitive with their peers and each other. While I occasionally have a pang of sorrow or guilt when my son with OA complains about having to wear glasses or about having to go with a vision teacher at school, I normally count our many blessings, not the least of which is that my son's ocular albinism is not unmanageable, not progressive, not life threatening and, has not prevented my son from doing anything he wants to do. "
>
> Vicky Vaught
> Conway, SC
> parent of a child with ocular albinism

While ocular albinism differs from oculocutaneous albinism, children with ocular albinism will face most of the same vision issues. Children with both conditions need assistive devices, individual education plans and accommodations for low vision and photophobia. Therefore the following chapters do not distinguish between children with OCA or OA, but refer to "children with albinism."

Hermansky-Pudlak Syndrome

Hermansky-Pudlak Syndrome, or HPS, is a rare type of albinism. HPS occurs in roughly one in one million births in the general population. However, this type of albinism is much more common in Puerto Rico, where one out of 1,800 people have HPS and one out of twenty-one people carry the gene for HPS. Families of Puerto Rican heritage are at much higher risk for this type of albinism. Although it is rare, a brief discussion of HPS is included here because the implications of having this type of albinism can be serious for children who are affected.

People with HPS exhibit the characteristics common to most types of albinism, such as decreased visual acuity, involuntary eye movement and varying degrees of hypopigmentation. However, people with HPS also have a bleeding disorder that can vary from mild to severe, and can even be life-threatening. Fifteen to 20 percent of people with HPS also develop a type of inflammatory bowel disease. This complication typically develops in the teen years or in early adulthood, but may begin in childhood. In addition, some people with HPS develop pulmonary fibrosis (a scarring of the lungs) between their late thirties and their fifties.

It is important for parents of children with albinism to be aware of this syndrome so they can alert medical professionals to its possibility in the event of unusual bleeding episodes. Testing for the syndrome is relatively easy. While most children with albinism will test negative for this syndrome, it is important to be aware of it if your child tests positive so doctors can better treat her in the event of a serious injury or surgery where bleeding complications may occur.

Testing for HPS

Currently, there is only one reliable test for HPS. A blood sample must be viewed under an electron microscope by someone trained to review blood platelet cells. Genetic testing for HPS is inconclusive because not

The story of Elizabeth Barnhill of Des Moines, Iowa, and her daughter, Nisha, illustrates why families should consider having their children tested for HPS. Nisha was adopted from India and when she arrived in the United States it became clear she would need surgery to repair a hole in her heart. Having read about albinism before bringing her daughter home, Barnhill decided to have Nisha tested as a precaution. She already suspected her new daughter might have HPS because Nisha seemed to bruise easily. Sure enough, Nisha tested positive for HPS. "Had I not had this information, my daughter would have gone into open heart surgery with no one knowing she had this bleeding disorder," says Barnhill. Instead, doctors were able to treat Nisha's bleeding and today she's a happy and healthy child.

Photo courtesy of Positive Exposure, Rick Guidotti

all the genes that cause HPS have been found. Thus, genetic testing for HPS can sometimes result in a false negative report.

Watching for Symptoms

The severity of HPS symptoms varies widely, so people with HPS may not show any signs of it, other than their albinism, for decades. Others, however, may develop symptoms even as young children. Many parents of children with HPS will notice that their child bruises easily, often for no apparent reason. Some children with HPS may experience nosebleeds that seem excessively frequent or last an abnormally long time. Most other complications do not appear until later in life, but parents of children with HPS should be on the lookout for digestive or breathing problems.

Treatments for HPS

While there is not yet a cure for HPS, many of its complications can either be treated or managed by a doctor who is aware of the syndrome. Dr. Samuel Seward runs a primary care practice for patients of all ages with HPS at Columbia University Medical Center in New York City. In addition to the typical precautions all people with albinism should take, such as good low vision care and avoiding sun burn, Dr. Seward advises his patients to be especially diligent about avoiding colds to prevent any unnecessary early damage to the lungs. He also strongly encourages patients with HPS to get the flu vaccine every year, and to get a pneumonia vaccine every five to seven years.

While HPS is not common, it has caught the attention of a number of prominent medical researchers because of what the disorder can teach scientists about many more common disorders. Currently the National Institutes of Health in Bethesda, Maryland, is conducting a number of research studies, and a number of other researchers around the country are working on mouse models to help develop better treatments for HPS. For more information, please visit **www.hpsnetwork.org**.

The Genetics of Albinism

A good way to learn about the genetics of albinism is to consult with a genetics counselor. Short of that, you may need to think back to high school genetics to understand what happens to cause a child to be born with albinism. **Keep in mind that, with the exception of ocular albinism described above, albinism occurs only when both parents carry an albinism gene and both parents pass it to their child.**

The DNA in our genes tells our bodies how to function. In very general terms, the DNA in the albinism gene does not contain the instructions for the body to make as much pigment as "normal." People have two copies of genes – one inherited from the father, the other inherited from the mother.

Most types of albinism are inherited in an "autosomal recessive" pattern. Each pregnancy is an independent event, a separate roll of the genetic dice. When two carriers of the same albinism gene have a baby, there is a one in four chance that the child will have albinism, one in two chance that the child will not have albinism but be a carrier and a one in four chance the child will not have albinism and not be a carrier.

Myths and Stereotypes

Now that you have a good understanding of what albinism is, we can dispel some of the myths associated with the condition. The most common one is that people with albinism have red eyes. They do not. At times, their eyes will have a reddish tint to them if the light hits them in a certain way, but most people with albinism have light blue or gray eyes. Some have hazel or brown eyes, and a few have violet eyes. The "red eyes" myth is particularly disturbing because it is so pervasive. People have been known to say, "She can't have albinism because she doesn't have red eyes."

Another common misperception about albinism is that it always results in a complete lack of pigment. There are many different types of albinism. Many people with albinism have some form of melanin and may tan slightly. People with albinism can have blonde hair, red hair, or even light brown hair.

Other myths include that the belief that a child with albinism will be blind. Albinism causes "low vision," or reduced visual acuity, but not blindness. Some people with albinism have vision that can be corrected to 20/200. People in this situation are called "legally blind" – an official designation that qualifies them for a variety of assistive services, but does not mean they are totally blind.

Less common, but equally untrue, are the myths that people with albinism are mentally impaired or have "special powers." Some people with albinism have been asked if they glow in the dark, or can see in the dark. The entertainment industry has perpetuated these myths by portraying people with albinism in stereotypical roles. We hope that time and increased advocacy will counter this negative portrayal.

Misinformation and the fear of differences are often at the root of these outlandish beliefs. You will have to develop patience and humor to deal with these perceptions. By doing so, you can help your child form a healthy attitude that will benefit her as an adult.

Some stereotypes and misperceptions may affect the way you perceive your child's potential in life. You may fear that your child will never dribble a basketball, never drive, never read or never enjoy sports. The degree of visual impairment associated with albinism varies from person to person, as does the impact of low vision on that person's life. The fact is that people with albinism participate in all kinds of sports, some are able to drive and many can read normal print. Letting your child discover her own abilities and set her own limits is the best way to determine how much of an impact albinism will have on her attitudes and experiences.

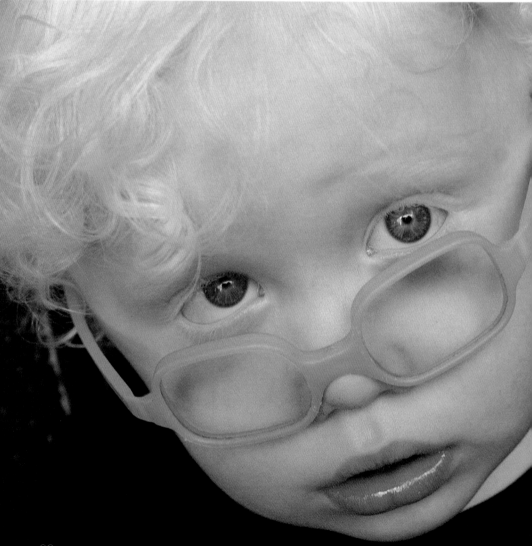

Chapter 3

Albinism's Impact on Vision and Development

Albinism affects people in varying degrees. Even two people with the same form of albinism will be impacted differently, but the following are some common effects:

- Albinism alters the structure of the eye and optic nerve.
- The eye usually lacks pigment, resulting in light sensitivity, or photophobia.
- The hair and eyes have little or no pigment.
- Reduced visual acuity is common as a result of the differences in the eye.
- These factors may cause short delays in reaching developmental milestones.
- Children with albinism may have some difficulty developing appropriate social skills.

This chapter explains the various ways in which albinism may impact your child's vision and development. It is impossible to create precise timelines for development, as each child grows and learns at his own pace. However, there are some guidelines and milestones that you should be familiar with as you watch your baby develop. As always, if you have questions or concerns, be sure to speak with your child's doctor.

Structure of the Eye

The eye develops differently in people with albinism, even before birth. Thus conventional treatments, such as surgery or eyeglasses, cannot correct the impairment. The eye problems associated with albinism result from a lack of pigment, and from physical differences in the optic nerve. In a typically pigmented person, light passes into the eye only through the pupil, which dilates to respond to the amount of light entering into the eye. The eye of a person with albinism has no pigment in the sclera (the 'whites' of the eyes) or the iris. As a result, the eye has no natural ability to regulate the amount of light that enters. Imagine the brightness of a floodlight that's always on, or the sensation of coming out of a dark movie theater on a sunny day – that is what it's like for someone with albinism.

The excess light is thought to impact the development of the retina. When albinism is present, the retina (the surface at the back the eye that receives light), does not develop normally before birth and in infancy. The nerve signals from the retina to the brain do not follow the usual nerve routes. Also, the iris does not have enough pigment to screen out stray light coming into the eye. The stray light impacts the development of the fovea, which is the part of the eye responsible for fine vision. The most common differences in the structure of the eye include:

- Reduced levels of pigment (melanin) in the iris and retina. A person's eyes usually appear to be violet, blue or gray in color. As a result of the lack of pigment, the eyes may appear reddish in certain light, or as a result of flash photography.
- Optic nerve fibers (ganglion cells) that improperly cross over to the opposite side of the brain as they link to the visual area of the brain (occipital cortex). This "miswiring" of the nerve cells gives the brain an abnormal signal, which decreases binocular vision (using both eyes) and poor stereopsis (depth perception) in most people with albinism.
- Foveal hypoplasia. The fovea is the part of the retina responsible for discerning fine detail. It is the center of the macula, which is the area of the retina responsible for the central, sharpest vision. In

people with albinism, this part of the retina does not develop and lacks pigment, and is the major cause of vision problems.

Impact on Vision

There is a wide range of visual acuity in people with albinism, and new parents often wonder where their child will end up on the vision spectrum. It is not possible to accurately predict during infancy what your child's vision will eventually be because vision development depends on many factors. In addition, there are a variety of adaptive devices that can help improve vision – and more are being developed all the time. The most important question will not be how much vision your child has, but how he uses the vision he does have.

People with albinism generally have what is called "low vision," which is a bilateral visual impairment that cannot be corrected by medical or therapeutic intervention, or by the use of specialized eyewear. Nonetheless, low vision can certainly be treated. The most common vision problems associated with albinism are:

Reduced Visual Acuity: Visual acuity refers to a person's ability to see fine detail. It is usually measured by reading letters on an eye chart. For most people with albinism, the best-corrected acuity can vary from between 20/30 to 20/400.

Light Sensitivity: The lack of pigment in the retina makes people with albinism highly sensitive to bright light and high glare, a condition called "photophobia." This extra sensitivity means that too much light reduces their ability to effectively use their vision. You will certainly notice your child cover his eyes or squint in bright light situations, which immediately reduces visual function.

Nystagmus: (Ni-STAG-mes) This is the term used for involuntary eye movement. Children born with albinism almost always have or develop nystagmus in the first few months after birth. Nystagmus is often the first sign or indication of albinism in infants with skin and hair color similar to their siblings or parents without albinism.

Nystagmus does not go away or disappear, but usually changes and becomes less noticeable with age. Nystagmus eye movement becomes more noticeable if a child is getting tired or feeling nervous or stressed. Nystagmus becomes less noticeable or may stop altogether when a child is asleep, nursing, relaxed or daydreaming, or if a person is sedated, suffers a head injury or drinks too much. This is just the opposite of what is expected or seen in people who do not normally have nystagmus. When they drink too much, are heavily sedated, or have a brain injury they may develop acute or sudden onset nystagmus. Police are sometimes trained to look for nystagmus in people they suspect may be intoxicated or drugged, and medical personnel are trained to look for nystagmus as a sign of brain injury and intoxication.

Therefore, it is important for parents, primary caregivers and people with albinism to alert nurses, doctors and first responders to a person's normal nystagmus to avoid misdiagnosis or mistreatment. Parents need to understand what nystagmus is, how it affects vision, and how to explain it to others when necessary.

With albinism, the nystagmus eye movement is commonly horizontal or side-to-side, but it may sometimes be vertical or rotary. A child's eyes may move smoothly and evenly, which is called pendular nystagmus, or the eyes may move faster in one direction and seem to quiver or jiggle in the other direction or in one location, which is called jerk nystagmus. The degree of movement side to side, up and down, or around, is called amplitude, and the speed of movement is called velocity. It is normal for amplitude and velocity of nystagmus to change with age.

Nystagmus has its own effect on vision, in addition to that of albinism. Because a child's eyes move involuntarily with nystagmus, they do not stay directly on target or continuously track what a child is trying to see. This does not mean a child with nystagmus sees only part of the time his eyes are open, but that the quality of the visual image may change as the eyes move. The stage of eye movement where there is best vision is called the foveation period, and it is the time the object of regard is focused on the fovea. Nystagmus decreases the amount of time the object is focused on the retina because of the involuntary eye movement.

Some children with nystagmus have what is called a "null point," which is the eye position in which nystagmus is at its minimum or is stopped. Some children do not develop a null point, while others have

Photo courtesy of Sandberg Photography, Christina Sandberg

more than one. It can also shift or change as vision develops with age. You may notice your child tilting his head to one side, or up or down – this is an attempt to find or use the null point to see better. A device called a nystagmograph measures null point, foveation period and the type of nystagmus a child has, and is generally used at an ocular motility lab or clinic. This measurement is usually made for research purposes or in preparation for various kinds of eye surgery. Surgery may be recommended in children with albinism and nystagmus to move null point closer to center if it is causing a substantial head turn or tilt that negatively affects physical activities or posture. Eye surgery may also decrease nystagmus temporarily or permanently.

If you do not have nystagmus and you turn in circles long enough and then stop you will induce or cause momentary nystagmus in yourself. You will feel dizzy and everything you see will keep moving after you stop turning, as your eyes continue to "spin." However, children with albinism and nystagmus do not see the world moving all the time (a condition called oscillopsia) and do not feel dizzy, despite constant eye movement. This is because their vision develops with nystagmus, and eye movement is normal to them. Your child's brain develops to accommodate nystagmus, and it is a normal part of his vision. In fact, changes in

41

eye movement in children and adults with albinism can signal changes in feelings or reaction to surroundings, and can even feel abnormal.

For more information on nystagmus, contact the American Nystagmus Network at **www.nystagmus.org**.

Strabismus: This is the technical term describes when the eyes are misaligned – when one eye turns in, out, up or down in relation to the other – and the eyes do not move in sync or maintain an equal distance because of a muscle imbalance. You can create the appearance of one type of strabismus, esotropia, by crossing your eyes. If one or both eyes turn out, it is called exotropia. Strabismus affects between two percent and five percent of the general population by most estimates. With albinism, strabismus is much more common, affecting as many as 50 percent of individuals with albinism. This is in part because of the effect of albinism on the eye-brain connection, making it more natural for people with albinism to see with each eye independently, instead of with stereopsis or both eyes together. One reason pediatric ophthalmologists like to see patients with albinism so often during infancy and toddler years is because of the higher incidence of strabismus with albinism, and because strabismus can be corrected.

Various types of treatments are available, depending on the type and severity of strabismus exhibited by the child. With "accommodative strabismus," both eyes, either alone or at the same time, may cross to improve focus. This type of strabismus is usually seen in people who have high refractive error, particularly hyperopia, also known as farsightedness. Glasses alone may correct accommodative strabismus.

The most common form of strabismus involves only one eye, and is caused by a different strength of vision or ability to focus in each eye. This type of strabismus may be corrected if it is caught early enough after onset. Treatment includes wearing an eye patch over the stronger eye, or putting drops in the stronger eye which cause it to blur. This encourages

When this type of strabismus is not corrected in early childhood, it may result in amblyopia, or the loss of some vision function, in the weaker eye. If you notice this kind of strabismus in your child, it is very important to seek medical attention.

the weaker eye to work more and develop stronger vision and better focus.

Surgery is available for all types of strabismus, and may be advised in early childhood if glasses, patching or drops don't correct the problem. Strabismus surgery is one of the most common types of eye surgery and is performed by a pediatric ophthalmologist. Since other conditions, such as an off-center null point, may be corrected by surgery at the same time as strabismus, a surgeon who has performed strabismus surgery on patients with nystagmus may be best suited to surgically address multiple issues associated with albinism at the same time.

Strabismus surgery, though not uncommon, does pose certain risks, such as scarring of the whites of the eyes at the corners, the potential need for additional surgery, and even a possibility of some double vision. Strabismus surgery requires general anesthesia but is usually performed as out-patient surgery. Patients' eyes are very red following surgery, but many children are eating ice cream and playing normally the same day with little or no sign of discomfort.

As with any medical procedure, parents should discuss and consider strabismus surgery carefully and be sure they are fully informed by their pediatric ophthalmologist about the necessity, options, risks and possible side effects. Parents who are confident and comfortable with a surgery decision may have children who are better prepared and less apprehensive. Parents should seek their doctor's advice on how to discuss strabismus surgery with their child and how to best prepare their child for the procedure.

Early Development

All babies and children are different, and hundreds of genetic, situational and environmental factors influence individual progress. Although it is important for you to have an idea of how children develop and when to start working on different skills, it is equally important to make certain modifications in your child's developmental timeline to accommodate the visual impairment associated with albinism.

Many new parents ask for a developmental chart for kids with albinism. They want to know when to expect their baby to roll over, make

Photo courtesy of Susan Leslie DuBois

eye contact, track objects or walk. This is not practical or possible for many reasons. Not only is there a wide range of visual acuity in children with albinism, there are also significant differences in how each child compensates or accommodates for his visual impairment. Parents of more than one child with albinism almost always have stories about how differently their children developed. It is more important to monitor your child's progress for signs of continual learning and improvement, than to track him on a set schedule for development.

> " Both of our children have OCA1a, and have developed very differently. When our son was born, he showed no signs of vision – he didn't make eye contact of track objects for almost six months. It was scary, and I'll never forget my joy when he "saw" for the first time. Our daughter was much different – she appeared to make eye contact from the very beginning, but was a much later walker. We realized that our children were just on different timelines – just like all kids. Our developmental pediatrician, as well as the early intervention specialists, helped us keep tabs on their development. "
>
> Susan Leslie DuBois
> Arlington, VA
> parent of two children with albinism

NOAH suggests that children with albinism commonly experience a two to three month delay in learning certain skills. Delays beyond that range may signify other issues, which is why it is important to discuss your concerns with your pediatrician, and why it is very important to enroll your child in early intervention services. The following factors specific to albinism will have an impact on how your child develops and may contribute to delays in some areas:

- reduced visual acuity
- photophobia, or sensitivity to light and glare
- trouble distinguishing items with low contrast
- difficulty with depth perception (an example would be changes between carpet and flooring)

Delays in visual skills are most noticeable in the first few months of life. Some children with albinism will not make eye contact, or will not fixate on objects; some will not turn their eyes to sound, and will not track objects. Experts believe the lack of pigment in the retina causes light rays to bounce around, making it difficult to focus on an image. The brain develops very quickly at this age, with new synapses formed every day. Between four and six months of age, the brain has developed to a point where vision seems to "kick in." At this age, most parents can expect to see:

- Fixation on a still object, presented six to ten inches from baby.
- Fixation on a slowly moving object, presented across the "midline" (the imaginary line that divides the body into right and left halves).
- Eye contact with a person who is fairly close and fairly still. At first, your baby may start looking at the light coming from behind an object, and it may look like he is looking at the top of your head or around the sides of your face, rather than directly at your face. This is a natural progression of his visual development.
- "Sound localization" may develop at this point. This means that your baby will turn his eyes in the direction of a sound.
- Reaching out towards a still object. Soon your child will also begin grasping for a moving object, as you start to slowly move a toy in different directions and then farther away.
- Tracking a moving object from side to side, then up and down, diagonally and in a circle.

Other delays may be observed in gross motor skills such as rolling over or establishing good neck and head control. A lack of visual input or the inability to observe others' behavior may contribute to these types of delays.

Your child's progress may vary, but you should measure his progress against his own abilities a month earlier. Keep notes and monitor progress in all developmental areas: cognitive function, fine and gross motor skills, language, social interaction and self-help skills. Your child may make progress in one area for a while, and then shift to another area. Keep a calendar handy and write a simple note to identify when your child does something new. These notes serve as good documentation tools to assist doctors and early intervention specialists in helping you evaluate your child's progress. Share these observations, along with any concerns you have, with your pediatrician or other health care provider.

Delayed Visual Maturation

While short developmental delays are common in children with albinism, a small percentage shows no signs of usable vision for the first few months of their lives. They do not seem to see anything – they do not make eye contact or track objects. This can be very frightening, but it is temporary. This "delayed visual maturation" is not thought to indicate less vision overall. It simply means the child's visual skills develop more slowly. When vision "kicks in," usually around five to six months of age, it seems to develop at the same rate as that of other children with albinism. In other words, delayed visual maturation does not indicate a more serious visual problem.

If you think your child has delayed visual maturation, talk to your doctor or vision specialist. Continue to present high-contrast materials and toys to your child, and do lots of talking and touching – as you would with any child with albinism. Do not be discouraged by a lack of response from your child, because even though it is difficult to know how much your child is absorbing, early stimulation is important.

Matt Bailey is an adult with albinism. The following is excerpted from his presentation at the 2004 NOAH Conference. Matt received a standing ovation for his description of how to look at the world through your child's eyes.

" What Do You See?

One of the most common and worrisome questions parents of children with albinism face is, "What does my child see?" Not knowing how well your daughter will be able to read her textbooks, if your son will be able to drive, or how your child's vision will affect his ability to participate in his favorite sport, can leave you feeling helpless and scared. While the effects of albinism on vision varies from person to person, there are some common traits in how people with albinism see. There's also a good chance that what your child can see out in the real world will turn out to be much better than the impression you got at that first eye doctor appointment.

People with albinism DON'T have blurry vision.

Normally sighted people are often baffled to hear that people with albinism do not have blurry vision. How can people with albinism have below-normal visual acuity, yet not have blurry vision? When normally sighted people experience vision problems, it's because the lens on the front of the eye is misshaped and can't focus correctly. That's what causes the blurry vision of nearsightedness, farsightedness, and astigmatism – problems with the eye focusing correctly. Normally

sighted people get glasses or contacts to correct the misshaped lens, restoring clear vision. People with albinism can also have farsightedness, nearsightedness and astigmatism. Glasses and contacts correct these eye conditions for people with albinism just as they do for normally sighted people. The eye problems people with albinism can't correct, however, involve the back of the eye.

Reduced Resolution

Imagine a large, clear color photo printed on the front page of the newspaper. Now imagine that someone in the photo is wearing a shirt with some lettering or a logo on the shirt pocket. You look closely at the photo, trying to read the lettering. To your dismay, you can't quite make it out. Overall, the picture isn't blurry. Yet when you look at the small details, you just can't discern them. If you were looking at the original photo the newspaper used, however, you could make out those words. You may have experienced the same effect if you've ever looked at a photo sent to you in an e-mail: neither picture was blurry, but the e-mail version doesn't quite have the same level of detail.

What's the difference between an original photo and a picture printed in the paper or sent to you in an e-mail? The difference is the resolution, or the number of dots that make up each picture.

The picture that forms on the back of the human eye is also made up of dots – millions and millions of them! They're the "cones" and "rods" on the retina in the back of the eye. Because of the lack of pigment, people with albinism have fewer of the cones than normally-sighted people have. Therefore, people with albinism have fewer "dots" in their picture of the world. The lower number of cones on the back of the eye is what causes lower visual acuity in people with albinism.

Want to see how different resolutions look? Visit an electronics store that has a large selection of TVs. First, check out one of the new High Definition Television (HDTV) sets. Then, look at the same picture on a comparably-sized, standard-definition TV. Neither TV has a blurry picture, but the image on the HDTV screen has a lot more subtle detail than the standard TV. The picture on the HDTV set looks so amazing because it has about five times more dots (pixels) on the screen than does the standard TV. In other words, the standard TV only offers one fifth the visual acuity of a new HDTV.

Depth Perception

You might hear that people with albinism have no depth perception. This statement is false. What is true, however, is that people with albinism generally do not have stereoscopic fusion, sometimes called stereopsis. Stereoscopic fusion is the process a normally-sighted person's brain performs automatically and subconsciously to compare what the left eye and the right eye see, creating a three-dimensional image from the information. However, stereoscopic fusion is just one method the brain uses to judge how far away things are.

Do you want to experience what the world looks like without stereoscopic fusion? Simply cover one eye! By doing so, you temporarily turn off your own stereoscopic fusion, since you're only seeing through one eye. Notice how you can still see the size of the room? You can still judge how far away people are? Go to your desk. Notice how you can still pick up a pen? Go to the kitchen. Notice how you can still get a glass from the cupboard? Go outside. See how you can still walk around? Notice you could still drive?

Instead of relying on your stereoscopic fusion to figure out how far away things are, you're now using perspective for your depth perception. Perspective relies on the fact that the world is an amazingly consistent place. Sofas, pencils, coffee mugs, cars, and people are all relatively consistent in size. There are no four-inch sofas or nine-foot coffee mugs. Therefore, the human brain can figure out how far away things are based on how large they look. The smaller the image, the farther away that object is. When you look down a long hallway, the brain knows the hallway isn't getting narrower; it simply appears narrower the farther down the hall you look.

If you walk up and down stairs with one eye covered, you might have some difficulty judging how far apart they are. People with albinism generally rely on subtle differences between how the light falls on each step to figure out how far apart steps are. If you have normal eyesight, you've always relied on your stereoscopic fusion to walk down stairs. Therefore, a toddler with albinism, who has always had to rely on subtle changes in appearance to judge steps, will probably have a better handle on stairs than you will with one eye closed.

There are a few areas where perspective isn't fully adequate for judging depth. Catching a baseball or hitting a tennis ball might be difficult for you with one eye covered, as it is for many people with albinism. That's because when a ball is falling from a blue sky, there is no object near the ball you can use to judge how far away the ball is. You can't rely on perspective to figure out the ball's location or speed. If the ball were rolling across the living room floor, however, you could instinctively use your knowledge of the floor to help you determine the location and speed of the rolling ball.

Common Questions

Why does my child hold some things right up to her eye to see them, yet she can see a tiny Cheerio dropped on the floor without any problem?

When your child holds an object close to her eyes, your child is inspecting the small details of that object. She's reading the letters or looking at the details of a picture on the side of her toy, or checking out the texture of the object itself. When your child spots a Cheerio or other small object in the carpet, your child isn't interested in the small details of the object. Your child can actually spot amazingly small objects, so long as she doesn't need to see the small details of the object. The "O" shape of a Cheerio is easy to recognize, especially lying on a floor that's a completely different color, so it stands out. Figuring out the difference between "i" and "l," or "O" and "Q," or "C" and "G," however, requires much greater detail and, therefore, a much larger picture on the back of the eye. Since bringing an object closer to the eye enlarges the image the object forms on the back of the eye, your child instinctively learns to do it.

Why does my baby seem a little bit uncertain about crawling or walking on steps, or from one room to another room?

Your baby shouldn't have any significant problems crawling and walking, although some babies with albinism might do so a little bit later than normally-sighted peers. However, he might be especially uncertain with stairs. Your baby might also seem hesitant about moving from room to room, especially if there's different flooring or carpeting in each room. Normally-sighted babies rely on stereoscopic fusion to see steps, but people with albinism often rely on subtle changes in appearance to figure out where steps are. Therefore, if your baby seems hesitant when encountering changing flooring, he may think the change in flooring is a large step. He's simply still working on learning what steps look like, versus what changes of flooring on the same level look like.

Why is my child able to spot McDonald's from the car window from so far away?

McDonald's has one of the easiest symbols to recognize of any business in history: the famous Golden Arches. Even with reduced visual acuity, a child can easily recognize this icon from far away. Similarly, your child might be able to recognize her favorite breakfast cereal before you can. If your child loves Apple Jacks, she doesn't have to see the words "Apple Jacks," she simply looks for the distinctive bright green color of the box to find it. People with albinism instinctively learn these tricks to help them find their favorite products. Those tricks, along with a high level of excitement for hamburgers and sweet-tasting cereals, often allow your child to spot the fast food and the sugary cereal before you do.

About the Numbers –
and Why They're Not that Bad

If your baby has just been diagnosed with albinism, it's understandable that you'll be eager to learn your child's visual acuity numbers. You're no doubt eager to have a clearer picture of how your child's vision will affect the things she will and will not be able to do. However, be aware that the visual acuity numbers might not give you an accurate idea of how your child will see in the real world. Fortunately, many parents find that their child's ability to perform everyday tasks out in the real world is actually much better than they feared when they first heard the numbers.

In addition to sharing your child's visual acuity with you in standard Snellen terms (such as 20/100, 20/200, 20/400), your child's eye doctor might tell you your child's vision in terms of a percentage: "Your baby sees 20/200 – that's ten percent of normal vision." This percentage tells you the resolution of your child's central visual acuity compared with that of a normally-sighted person. This percentage does NOT, however, mean that your child will only see ten percent of the world around him, or that your child will only be able to do ten percent of the things she wants to do. Think about a new high definition TV compared with a standard TV. The high definition TV has five times higher resolution – equivalent to the difference between 20/20 vision and 20/100 vision – and certainly offers an impressive picture. But do you actually see five times more on the high definition TV picture?

Scientists believe that the brains of normally-sighted people only process one percent of what their eyes actually see. The remaining 99 percent of visual information simply isn't needed for the tasks of everyday life. Therefore, if your child's doctor tells you your child only has ten percent of her vision, it might mean your child's brain ignores only 90 percent of what her eyes see, instead of 99 percent. In other words, although there will certainly be times when your child's reduced vision will prevent her from seeing something, or require her to use special tools and techniques to see it, there will be plenty of occasions where your child's eyes will provide her brain more than enough visual information to perform life's tasks.

When your child looks at the natural beauty of the world, she might not see each individual blade of grass, but she will still see the rich beauty of a lush green meadow. Your son might not see a bird hiding in a tree, but he will still look with awe at the trees in the forest. When you take your family to the beach, your child with albinism might not see the ripple of every wave, but albinism won't prevent your child from seeing the amazing richness of the orange sun rising or setting over the blue water.

Matt Bailey
Chapel Hill, NC
adult with albinism

Chapter 4

Stimulating Your Child's Vision

Infants and children learn constantly. Every sight, sound, smell, touch and taste provides an educational experience for little ones. Vision plays an important role in early childhood development, and when vision is impaired, certain modifications must be made to give your child the same learning opportunities as children who are totally sighted. In addition, there are many things you can do to help stimulate the development of your child's vision. This chapter discusses strategies to stimulate all of your child's senses, and ways to adapt visual learning in children with albinism.

Vision develops a great deal over the first year of a child's life. Newborn babies cannot see anything farther than eight to twelve inches away, and eyesight develops gradually over the first eight months of life. Typically-sighted children cannot discern color until they are approximately four months old, and do not develop 20/20 vision until they reach approximately six to eight months of age. The child with albinism will develop in a different way, and it is very difficult to tell how far away a baby with albinism can see.

However, it is important to provide your baby with stimulating visual experiences to help her brain develop. As her brain develops, so does her ability to see more, giving her the tools she needs to understand and manage her environment. As discussed earlier, it is more important for your child to show continuous development, than to follow any particular time frame.

Infants

Babies and children with visual impairments may not respond visually or appear to look at you or at toys. If this is the case with your child, be patient, continue to play with her and provide appropriate forms of stimulation. Your child's eyes and vision may take longer to mature, and her brain may take longer to form the pathways that allow her to interpret what she is seeing. Regardless of how much your baby can process visually, it is important that you connect with her in a meaningful way. When she is very young, your voice and your touch are the most important tools you have to reach her.

Use real-world stimulation activities as much as possible, employing objects and events that your child will encounter on a daily basis. Carry your baby in a front-carrier whenever practical, and provide her with a running commentary on your activities. Use descriptive language to help her connect with what you are doing. The following activities and strategies can help you stimulate your baby's vision and development.

Gross Motor Skills

Some children who are visually impaired have slight delays in developing gross motor skills, which use the body's large muscles, including the legs, arms and trunk. You can help your child by adapting common activities to encourage movement. All babies benefit from "tummy time" to help them build muscle strength to raise their head, neck, torso and upper body. These are prerequisite skills for pushing up, crawling, changing positions and sitting. Initially, your child may not have the same visual incentives to raise her head off of the floor as children who are not visually impaired. To help her look up, use toys with sounds and lights. Once your baby lifts her head off the floor:

- Start using a solid, dark-colored blanket for tummy time. The dark blanket will reduce the amount of glare and encourage looking at toys on the blanket.
- Place objects and toys around baby that provide ample contrast to the dark blanket. Keep in mind that young infants have a limited ability to discriminate colors for a while.
- Place several objects and toys around your baby so no matter

where she looks, she will see something. Experiment with the distance between your child and the objects. Once your child locates the toy visually and responds to it, move the toy a little farther to encourage your child to search, scan and eventually begin reaching for the toy.

- Roll a toy train or car on the ground to encourage visual tracking. Incorporate sound into the activity by calling out, "choo choo" or "honk, honk," especially if baby is not yet visually locating the toy. Encourage baby to locate the toy using the auditory clue.

When your baby is old enough to face forward in a front carrier, you can include her in all of your activities by describing what is going on around her. For example, as you walk into the kitchen, you can say, "Here we are, going into the kitchen, and we're going to wash our hands. When we turn the handle on the faucet – water comes out!" Put your baby's hands in the water and let her splash. This will help her begin to form the connections that she might otherwise miss. Stand with her very close to a mirror, raise her arms up and say, "So big!" This will help strengthen her eye contact, and is just plain fun.

Hold your baby close to you. It provides an excellent position in which to accommodate your baby's vision since your face is in close proximity to your baby's. Remember, a baby who is visually impaired may not make eye contact or look at your face. You can encourage your child's vision by placing a soft light behind your head. Make sure the light is not too bright and does not shine in your baby's eyes. (Try a light shining upward on the ceiling.) The light will create an illuminated "halo" around your head and provide greater contrast when your baby does look at your face. Make silly, loving and surprised facial expressions and be overly expressive with your gestures. Try moving your face a few inches from your baby's face so your child can see you more clearly. Some mothers use bright lipstick to highlight their mouths, and some parents wear a clown nose to draw attention to their face.

With your baby in your lap, facing outward, take a toy and slowly move the toy in and out of her view. Hold the toy high over your baby's head and slowly move it down to the center. Do the same from well below the baby's chin and move the toy up to her eye level. Now move the toy from behind her ears, along the side of her head until she can

see it approaching from the side. If your child is just not locating the toy visually, you can gently touch the toy to the child. You may need to hold the toy just a few inches away from your baby so she can see it best. It may also help if the toy squeaks or rattles.

Cognitive Development

To help your child make visual connections, choose toys with simple, high-contrast patterns. Bold patterns are easiest for all babies to see, especially infants who are visually impaired. Avoid busy, over-detailed patterns on toys and blankets at first.

Use light as an incentive, and to illuminate special toys. Even though your child will be sensitive to light, all children are mesmerized by a dancing beam of light, and soft lights are pleasing to children who are visually impaired. Try a soft light or flashlight to encourage your baby to look up, and focus the beam on a toy, your hand or the wall. Also, there are many toys available that project images on walls and ceilings.

Place high-contrast images near your baby's head while she is in the crib or play pen, and attach a high contrast play mat to the back of your car seat so that she has an engaging image to look at when riding in the car. Try using a variety of objects near her feet. At first, place a rattle toy or a stuffed animal for her to kick, or try a kick piano. You also may want to get wrist rattles and socks with rattles in them, as all babies discover their feet at some point.

Baby gym mats are great to use while your baby is on her back. You can use linking rings to suspend a toy over her to encourage swatting. **Since many babies who are visually impaired swat at toys later than their sighted peers, you can make sure toys are dangling near your baby's extremities so she will hit them when moving normally.** A baby gym with a series of lights that flash to music is a good choice for a baby with albinism. The goal is for your baby to follow the rhythmic pattern of lights to the songs that are played as each light is turned on and off by the toy. Eventually, this will encourage her to look to the sides at the lights, which promotes neck muscle development.

Read books with your baby from birth on. Try using "foil" books whose sheen attracts an infant's eyes to the pages, and whose crinkly

Photo courtesy of Positive Exposure, Rick Guidotti

pages give tactile and auditory feedback. These books are simple and have shiny pictures of different objects encountered in daily life. Look for books that have large pictures and clear, large, simple words.

A good activity for your baby is to placer her in a "high contrast seeing circle." First, place her on a solid, dark blanket, and dim the lights in the room. Place a selection of high-contrast toys in a semi-circle around her top half. Shine a flashlight on each item, waiting until she locates the illuminated toy. Then move the light to another item.

Body Position During Play

As your baby begins to sit independently, you may notice she looks closely at toys and objects, which causes her to lean over and lose her balance. This can delay her ability to develop the muscles she needs for stable sitting. Encourage proper sitting posture by raising your child's play platform part of the time. Provide a low, safe object to place toys on so your baby does not lean so far over to see her toys.

A play platform can consist of a sofa pillow, a very low child's table, or even a bed tray. Some toys are designed for a baby to sit at and you can put other toys on them as well. By using the raised play platform periodically you will encourage correct posture. Once your baby has developed better posture you can take the raised play platform away and allow her to lean over to look at toys. She will need to build the strength to move from the leaning position to a straight sitting position. People with visual impairments often have neck and back fatigue from leaning over to see items up close. By putting toys on a raised play platform, you will alleviate some of the neck fatigue and increase your child's play and learning time.

Toddlers and Young Children

Once your infant is better able to see and track objects, you can help her become more observant and learn how to scan the environment to look for something. There are endless possibilities for doing this in your everyday routine.

The Grocery Store

Have your child help you find the "orange" carrots in the produce department. Your child's visual acuity may not provide her with much detail to see the actual individual carrots, but she may be able to see the "orange" vegetable situated between the green ones. Next time, ask her to find the "green" apples. Point out that the green apples are a lighter shade than the broccoli.

As your child's observational skills and acuity develop more, she can help identify other groceries. Ask her to find the gallon of milk with the blue lid, have her locate her favorite breakfast cereal, which can be hard to discriminate because of the complex detail on the boxes. Your child may have to get close to the boxes of cereal to examine them. Encourage her to take her time to find the right one. Next time, she may remember where it was located and find it more quickly, which is a compensatory skill that aids her visual efficiency.

> My experience as an optometrist taught me a lot about vision, but watching my daughter who has albinism grow up has taught me more. Lee-Anne manages quite well, and has always compensated for her visual impairment. The truth is, this is not unusual for those with albinism. Once, we were in the grocery store, and both of us were looking for a particular brand of cereal. She found the box before I did. Why did this happen? Upon careful questioning she told me she looked for the pattern of colors on the box. In the same way, she found the can of frozen lemonade before I did.
>
> Rick Thompson, OD
> Ontario Canada
> parent of a child with albinism

Balloons, Bubbles and Balls

Encourage your child to track the movement of a balloon or bubbles or other items that move down, up and away. Play keep-the-balloon-up by batting it between the two of you while inside, or even outside when glare and bright sunlight are not at issue. Play with sticky or rubbery balls or under-inflated balls in bright colors because they are easier to catch. Start by rolling the ball to your toddler and progress to bouncing it lightly to her. Once she is comfortable with these activities, try throwing it to her gently from different distances. These activities will help her develop fine motor skills and hand-eye coordination.

> "Playing with bubbles is an activity that I could have never imagined Lyra being able to do when she was first diagnosed with albinism. It was one of the many things that I worried that she would never get to experience. Well, Lyra CAN pop bubbles… and chase them and point to them and stomp on them and even tries to eat them! She was even able to follow and point to bubbles I'd blown when we were playing outside in less than optimal lighting conditions. I get so excited when I see her able to really see things that I didn't expect."
>
> Mashawna Thompson
> Edwardsville, KS
> parent of a child with albinism

The "I Spy" Game

You can also play "I Spy" with your child as a way to challenge her to notice her surroundings and to learn through observation. It might seem unproductive to challenge your child in this way – particularly if you also have children who are typically-sighted. However, your child's capacity for vision will surprise you, and you should give her the opportunity to stretch her skills. Start with a really large object, such as a fire truck or a school bus. The goal is to encourage your child to use her vision to observe the world around her. You can always give clues to help your child succeed. You can also use this game when reading books to your child. Ask her to find the puppy in the picture, or to identify what a certain character is wearing.

Some parents worry about frustrating their child by challenging her too often to identify objects she cannot see. **Keep in mind that your child really will see more than you think. Don't let your perception of her limitations create barriers.** A cow in a pasture might not be as clear as it would be to you, but your child can still discern the shapes and colors of things in the distance. Also, playing vision games with your child will give you a clearer sense of what she can see, and will give her valuable practice in using her vision.

Extending Your Child's "Visual Reach"

While you cannot actually improve the way your child's eyes work, there are several ways you can help her use her vision more effectively. The term "functional vision" refers to how well a person uses vision in different environments for specific tasks and for gathering incidental information, such as noticing things. "Visual efficiency" refers to how well a person uses her vision in relation to her visual capacity (the amount a person can actually see).

In other words, if you think of vision as a tool, functional vision relates to how well one uses the tool in general, while visual efficiency relates to how much of the tool one uses. A child could have lower functional vision, but use it very efficiently – and "see" more than a person with better vision, but less visual efficiency. Our goal as parents is to encourage our children to increase their functional vision, and to extend their visual reach by increasing their visual efficiency. There are several ways to increase your child's visual reach:

- Encourage visual curiosity. Have your baby follow a bouncing balloon that gets closer and closer. Blow bubbles and then have your child chase and pop them. Play hide and seek. Encourage your child to find her own toys in the toy chest. Allow an older child to play with a remote-controlled car. These activities will help your child learn that using her vision is rewarding.

- Teach your child that other people use their vision to access information, and learn by observing.

- Help your child understand that with an "extension" (monocular, glasses) she may see what others see.

Stimulating the Other Senses

Although you may feel compelled to work most on vision skills, it is important to spend adequate time stimulating auditory (hearing) and tactile (touch) senses too. Language and motor development are equally important. Developing these senses will enable your child to become a well-rounded learner and provide her with compensatory skills to offset her visual impairment.

Touch

Some children with low vision have "tactile sensitivity," meaning they are reluctant to touch different textures. For example, some children will not touch grass or wet sand with their bare feet, while others will not finger-paint or play with clay. To overcome this sensitivity, let your child play with toys and objects that have different textures, bumps, shapes, fabrics and feelings. Continue to introduce different textures to your child, and if she resists them, don't force her, but try again at a later date. Many common household items can provide your child with a wide range of sensory experiences:

- Let your child play with sandpaper, a colander, a basting brush or a prickly doormat.
- Expose your child to different cloth textures, such as silk, corduroy, denim, terry cloth or fleece.
- Offer your child one of the children's books with textured pages that feel like a furry puppy, a bumpy lizard or a rough cat's tongue. Some books even have tactile or raised letters for children to trace.
- Play with clay or finger-paint with whipped cream or pudding – a fun way to experiment with textures and overcome tactile sensitivity.
- Bury small toys or letter magnets in a bowl of uncooked rice or beans. Encouraging your child to dig around will help overcome sensitivities, and also develop fine motor skills.

Auditory Stimulation

Expose your baby to a variety of sounds, rhythms, music styles, languages, tones and voices. As your baby continues to develop, play listening games in which you ring a fun bell and encourage your child to turn toward the sound. Encourage good listening skills in your child, as she will use these skills later on in school to compensate for her low vision.

Many children love music and there are a wide variety of toys that help develop auditory skills. Inexpensive compact disc players can be a great way to introduce your child to music (and also help her develop fine motor skills by manipulating the buttons). Listening to one of the many popular children's books and stories on compact disc or audio tape can also help increase auditory skills.

Smell and Taste

Discuss these senses with your child and make your child aware of how these senses are used. Allow your child to participate in age-appropriate cooking activities and enjoy food with different tastes and textures. Three year-olds love to experiment with smells. Try a "science experiment" in which you set out small bowls with different items: cinnamon, cumin, vanilla, cloves, garlic, lemon or coffee. Ask your child to identify whether the substance is sweet, spicy or sour. Play games with your child that require the use of a couple of senses, such as looking at a letter, feeling it and then listening to the sound the letter makes. By stimulating multiple senses together, your child will be able to compensate for any lost information from the visual impairment and will learn to hone the use of other senses.

Looking Ahead: The Older Child

There are some great games and toys that will help your older child strengthen fine motor skills and coordination. Air hockey promotes hand-eye coordination; marble track games help develop fine motor skills and visual tracking skills; even video games can help develop visual skills. Working on puzzles helps children develop spatial and visual skills, as well as fine motor skills.

To help develop balance and gross motor skills, get your child a scooter, and encourage her to ride it. It is easier than a bicycle, and will help her develop the skills necessary to successfully ride a bicycle. Riding on a bicycle extension that attaches to an adult frame is a good intermediate step that can build your child's confidence and allow her to get used to the balance needed to ride a bike.

In-line skates, roller skates and ice skates are also great tools for developing athletic ability and gross motor skills. And don't overlook simple playground games like hopscotch and jumping rope. These games can be fun ways for your child to develop coordination, as well as social skills.

Photo courtesy of Susan Leslie DuBois

Teaching Your Child to Ride a Bike

Some children with albinism have no fear of riding a bicycle, and are easy to teach. Others have difficulty with depth perception and glare, and are reluctant to give it a try. If your child is hesitant to learn, don't give up, but don't pressure her, either. Start slow, with a smaller bicycle than you think your child needs, and head for a large parking lot. A smaller bicycle keeps your child closer to the ground, and is easier to control. Training wheels are an important first step, but don't take them off with the expectation that your child will ride away wobble-free. When she seems ready, try taking both the training wheels and the pedals off at the same time and let her wheel around a parking lot for a while. Gliding without having to pedal will develop balance, and you can teach your child how to put a foot down quickly to break a fall. Give your child lots of time to learn. Riding a bicycle is an important part of childhood, and while sometimes more difficult for kids with low vision, it is certainly within reach. Celebrate the transition to two wheels with the purchase of a cool bell or a new helmet.

Mobility Skills and Your Daily Routine

As a parent, you play a key role in helping your children understand the world around them. During early childhood, mobility skills develop based on logic, pattern recognition, common sense, experience and exposure to the environment. Some families engage the services of a Certified Orientation and Mobility Specialist for reasons that will be addressed later in the book, but if you do not have or need such services, there are many things you can do on your own to help your child develop the skills necessary to navigate the world with confidence.

Directions, Spatial Awareness and Route Planning

From infancy on, use specific spatial terms when interacting with your child such as up, down, under, over, left, right, behind, in front of, next to, long and short. Familiarize your child with movement directions using descriptive verbs: "We are going into the kitchen to get your bottle." As your child gets older, encourage her to:

- Memorize her home address.
- Provide directions home using descriptors such as "turn left" and "turn right."
- Identify visual landmarks, such as "the gas station at corner of my street."
- Identify tactile landmarks, such as, "My house is after the second speed bump."

When traveling with your small child, make a game out of identifying the landmarks you encounter. You can make up songs, such as, "Up the hill, swerve with the curve, through the light, turn right and we are home for the night!" These games not only promote spatial and directional awareness, they give your child learning tools to aid with memorization.

Once your child has mastered basic spatial and directional concepts, start adding more abstract vocabulary such as the terms north, south, east and west. Explaining that the sun rises in the east and sets in the west is a good starting point for enhancing these concepts. Discuss where familiar destinations are located, and what direction they are from your home as you travel with your child. Ask questions such as, "Here is the bank, out your window. Is this where we turn to get home?" You can also provide information such as, "Your pre-school is one mile west of our house, right down Elm Street." Ask if she recognizes where she is when on a familiar street, and give frequent verbal cues. This will expose her to these concepts on a continuing basis.

Keep in mind that directions are very difficult for many people, visually impaired or not. However, your child will one day have to figure out bus routes, maps and how to get around a city, campus or office complex. Fostering good observational skills at an early age will help your child throughout her life. Some children have a very difficult time grasping these concepts, so be patient if it takes your child years to understand directions. Keep using these terms in your daily travels, which will increase your child's exposure to these concepts.

Pattern Recognition and Logic for Mobility Skills

Help your child recognize patterns and use logic to foster good mobility. In most cases, addresses and room numbers follow some sort of pattern. As a person who is visually impaired, your child may not perceive the pattern as quickly as a child who is sighted. However, your child can use logic to figure out where she is and where she needs to go.

- Help your child understand the way rooms are numbered in buildings. If the doctor is in Suite 401, teach your child that the four means you have to travel to the fourth floor. Ask your child to help you find the elevator or the stairs.
- Help her identify clues to locate the elevator, such as doors that do not swing open. Let your child figure out which button to push to go up in the elevator. Ask, "Which one would make the most sense? Is it the one on top or the one on the bottom?" Have your child listen for the "ding" the elevator may make before its doors open. Direct her to move to the elevator that made the sound. While in the elevator, count together the number of beeps for each floor until you reach the fourth floor. If you are taking the stairs, point out landmarks that indicate each floor, such as the door with a number on it, a larger landing and the number of stairs you have to climb between each floor. Count the stairs together and count the floors too.

- When using the restroom, point out to your child that the word "women" is longer than the word "men" on restroom doors. The word "elevator" is longer than the word "stairs." Your child may not be able to read yet and may not be able to see the individual letters, but may see well enough to tell which word is bigger than the other.

By allowing your child to be an active participant in finding destinations, you are helping her develop a sense of spatial and pattern awareness, logic, and compensatory skills. Remember that as your child grows, she may be able to see the numbers on the elevator and the signs on the doors of the floors, but she also has a set of compensatory skills to use to offset her visual impairment. These skills will not only help your child navigate and locate destinations using logic, but will encourage pattern recognition, which enhances intellectual development.

Promoting Independent Travel

While some people with albinism do drive a car, it is possible that your child will not drive as an adult. It is important for your child to see and, when possible, to experience alternative methods of transportation. Use other modes of transportation not only for fun, but to run errands, go to play dates and other daily activities. If at all possible, walk to the library, take the bus or subway to the museum, or ride in a taxi to an appointment. If this is not feasible, perhaps you can talk about people you know who live in cities or near mass transportation. Library books are a good way to expose your child to other means of travel. Or perhaps you can use public transportation when you are on vacation. The goal is for your child to become comfortable and familiar with forms of transportation beyond just the car.

Educational Resources

The Hadley School for the Blind offers a wide range of free distance learning courses for parents of children with visual impairments. Topics include orientation and mobility, social skills and daily living skills. Please see their website at **www.hadley-school.org** or the Resource Section for more information.

Chapter 5

Medical Professionals and the Eye Exam

You are most likely to receive your child's diagnosis of albinism from your pediatrician, whose knowledge about albinism may be quite limited. It is highly likely that you will quickly know more about albinism than your doctor, but his or her knowledge about child development and health will be invaluable in tracking your child's progress. Your pediatrician will also be your earliest resource for medical information, assessments and referrals. When selecting a doctor, look for a "developmental pediatrician" who specializes in treating children with various medical conditions that can impact development. If you do not feel comfortable or supported by your pediatrician, you may want to make a change.

This chapter explains the different types of doctors you will encounter and the different medical tests and treatments often administered, suggests how best to be an effective advocate for your child and offers practical tips on getting the most from your doctor's appointments.

Medical Specialists

Any one of a number of medical specialists may see a child with albinism in his early years. These include a general optometrist, a low vision optometrist, a pediatric ophthalmologist (PO) or a pediatric neuro-ophthalmologist (PNO). At some point in your child's development, you may also consult other professionals, including a geneticist, a genetic counselor, a teacher for the visually impaired (TVI), an occupational therapist (OT), a dermatologist and a Certified Orientation and Mobility Specialist (COMS).

Eye Specialists

An ophthalmologist is a physician who specializes in the medical and surgical care of the eyes and visual system, and in the prevention of eye disease and injury. The ophthalmologist performs routine eye exams and diagnoses and treats eye disorders and diseases. He or she also provides prescriptions for eyeglasses, performs surgery and cares for eye problems caused by systemic illness.

An optometrist is not a medical doctor, but is a doctor of optometry (OD). Optometrists diagnose vision problems and eye disease, prescribe eyeglasses and contact lenses, and prescribe drugs to treat eye disorders. They cannot perform surgery, but they often provide patient care before and after eye surgery. Sometimes ophthalmologists and optometrists work in the same practice and co-manage patients.

Both general optometrists and ophthalmologists have extensive training in detecting and treating a wide variety of eye conditions and diseases. Both can prescribe lenses and medications for eye conditions. While only ophthalmologists perform surgery, optometrists generally have more training in lenses, contact lenses, low vision and vision therapy. Both professions are ethically and legally required to refer to another practitioner any patient needing care outside their area of expertise.

An optician is trained to follow a prescription from an optometrist or ophthalmologist to grind, fit and dispense eyeglasses and contact lenses. The optician is also skilled in finding glasses or lenses that fit properly and comfortably, which is an important part of getting a child to wear glasses.

A pediatric ophthalmologist (PO) is trained to prescribe lenses and specializes in childhood eye disease and eye surgery. This specialist often has experience with patients with albinism. A pediatric neuro-ophthalmologist (PNO) has additional training in neurological conditions and diseases affecting the eye, including optic nerve disease, tumors involving the visual system, brain injury, strabismus and nystagmus. A PNO is often consulted because neurological problems other than albinism may cause the appearance of a small optic nerve, strabismus, and nystagmus.

Low vision optometrists and low vision ophthalmologists specialize in treating patients with low vision, and often have experience with children with albinism too. These eye doctors will assess the visual needs of the individual and prescribe special adaptive devices to suit those needs.

The practitioners who specialize in low vision treatment are arguably the most important for people with albinism. In fact, many families switch from an ophthalmologist to a low vision specialist when their children are still quite young and their vision stabilizes. The theory is that an ophthalmologist is trained to treat vision that has deteriorated in some way, while a low vision specialist is trained to help maximize a limited amount of vision. If you cannot find a low vision specialist in your area, consider traveling to a nearby city once a year when your child reaches school age.

Genetic Specialists

A geneticist is a medical doctor who specializes in the study of genetics. Some families elect to see a geneticist to determine what type of albinism runs in their family. Certain types of albinism, including Hermansky-Pudlak Syndrome, may prompt other serious health concerns. A clinical geneticist will evaluate, diagnose and treat genetic diseases. A geneticist will review individual and family histories, examine clinical records and interview patients or parents to construct a family history. They may also examine patients to determine the need for laboratory or other testing and make the appropriate referrals for those tests.

A genetic counselor is a health professional with a graduate degree and experience in medical genetics and counseling. Genetic counselors may enter the field through a variety of disciplines, including biology, genetics, nursing, psychology, public health and social work. Although genetic counselors are not medical doctors, they work as valuable members of a health care team, providing information and support to families who have members with birth defects or genetic disorders, and to families who may be at risk for a variety of inherited conditions. Genetic

counselors identify families at risk, investigate the problem present in the family, interpret information about the disorder, and analyze inheritance patterns and risks of recurrence. They also review available options with the family and suggest helpful resources in the community.

If a couple has a child with albinism and becomes pregnant again, they may choose to have the fetus tested for albinism. The test uses amniocentesis (inserting a needle into the uterus to draw off fluid). Cells in the fluid are then examined to see if they contain an albinism gene from each parent. Those considering prenatal testing should be made aware that people with albinism usually adapt quite well to their disabilities and lead very fulfilling lives. For specific information on genetics and testing, seek the advice of a qualified genetic counselor. Genetic counselors are usually associated with universities and children's hospitals. The National Society of Genetic Counselors maintains a referral list, available at **www.nsgc.org**.

Dermatologists

A dermatologist is a doctor who specializes in the diagnosis and treatment of diseases of the skin. People with albinism must pay close attention to the health of their skin because their lack of pigment increases the risk of sun damage and skin cancer. Your child should see a dermatologist at least once in the first eighteen months of his life. A dermatologist will be able to answer your questions about sun exposure and protection, as well as examine your child to establish a baseline for his skin health. The dermatologist will also be able to assess the possible development of pigment, which can occur with some forms of albinism.

As your child grows, it is very important to closely watch his skin health, and to look for moles that have changed or look unusual, as well as other lesions that may grow, bleed and crust over continually but do not heal. Contact your doctor if you notice brown or black streaks underneath or bordering your child's fingernails, a pigmented mass in his mouth or a dark spot on his eye. You can learn more and also search for a dermatologist in your area on the website of the American Academy of Dermatology, at **www.aad.org**.

Chapter 12 discusses sun safety and skin protection more fully.

What to Expect at the Eye Exam

When you make an appointment for your child's eye examination, try to schedule it for early in the day, when the doctor's office is less likely to be backed up, and your child is less likely to be tired. Bring snacks and quiet toys in case you have to wait. For a very young child, you may want to bring a favorite toy that lights up, which can also assist the doctor during the eye exam. It is a good idea to write down any questions you have before the examination, and bring a pad of paper and a pen to take notes. You should also give your child an age-appropriate explanation of what to expect during the exam. A young child may appreciate having a blanket or stuffed animal to snuggle with.

Be sure to bring all referrals and the necessary paperwork. Make sure your child is healthy and well-rested and is not hungry. If your baby or very young child is upset or uncooperative, try wrapping him in a blanket or holding him on your lap to help him feel secure. He may need a short break during the exam, or a small snack. If he won't keep his eyes open, a tool called a lid speculum may be used to gently hold the eyes open just long enough to allow for the a particular test to be completed. Older children can usually be talked into cooperating, but the prospect of a special treat like a lollipop can be very persuasive.

Internal and External Physical Examination of the Eye

The eye examination itself requires the examiner, whether an optometrist or ophthalmologist, to assess eye structure and function. The doctor will assess refractive error and visual acuity, perform an internal and external physical examination of the eye and measure eye movement and eye position.

The examiner will first look at the overall appearance of the eyes and facial structure, then use a penlight, slit lamp and ophthalmoscope to examine the eyes more closely. One of the first things the doctor will look for is transillumination of the iris in each eye. This is an important test for differentiating albinism from other conditions. This test is performed using a penlight or slit lamp (a microscope fixed to an examination table) in a totally dark room. The light is transmitted through the iris much like a flashlight shines through fabric under certain lighting conditions. Transillumination will reveal an absence of pigment in the eye, and is the easiest way to identify albinism. You may worry these tests will be painful for your child because of the bright light produced by these instruments, but the child is usually just momentarily uncomfortable, and the tests are an important part of the diagnostic process.

The doctor will also assess your child's eye movement and position to identify the level and type of nystagmus and the null point. He or she will look at the alignment of your child's eyes to determine whether strabismus is an issue of concern. In addition, the external examination will include checking the conjunctiva, the cornea and the iris for appropriate development.

To accurately assess your child's vision, the doctor may use eye drops to dilate the pupil and relax the ciliary muscle that focuses the eye for near point work. These drops are available in various strengths. Some last a few hours while others can keep the pupils dilated for up to a week. Sometimes the eye drops will sting, so the doctor will use a "numbing drop" first. Always ask if this step is possible, and explain it to your child when practical.

If your child is over the age of two, ask before the appointment whether his eyes will be dilated. It will allow you to explain the process to him beforehand, so he is not surprised. Keep in mind that eye exams will be a regular part of your child's life, and any helpful patterns you establish while he is young will make the early years much easier. When a child trusts his doctor or optician, he is more likely to cooperate.

Evaluation of Visual Acuity

The visual acuity for people with albinism can be corrected with eyeglasses or contact lenses to anywhere from 20/30 to 20/400. However, there are several different measures of acuity, including unaided acuity, corrected acuity, monocular acuity, binocular acuity and near acuity. It is helpful to know some definitions.

Unaided acuity is measured without the use of eyeglasses, contact lenses or low vision devices.

Aided acuity is measured with the aid of eyeglasses or contact lenses. This is the most widely used acuity measure for determining vision impairment.

Monocular acuity is measured with one eye occluded or covered. This is measured for each eye, and can be recorded as aided and unaided. Because the nystagmus increases when one eye is covered, the monocular acuity is usually less than the binocular acuity.

Binocular acuity is measured with both eyes open. This can also be recorded as aided and unaided. The aided binocular acuity is probably the most useful measurement when predicting visual function for everyday tasks.

Near acuity is measured using a near-point chart, usually at a distance of sixteen inches or forty centimeters. Near acuity testing may include describing pictures or reading individual letters, words or continuous text. Those with albinism tend to have better near acuity than distance acuity since the nystagmus is reduced at near focus and the light levels are better controlled. This testing needs to be done as the child approaches the reading age. This test must be done prior to the use of the dilating eye drops to be valid.

Your child's age and ability to respond will determine the type of test used to evaluate his visual acuity. For example, a six-month-old will not be able to read the letters on an eye chart, while a five-year-old is most likely able to respond to direct questions, and will recognize most letters.

The Preferential Looking Technique may be used for infants and young children. Because infants prefer looking at patterns, this test involves showing the child two targets. The first target has no pattern and the second has black lines. This second target has lines or stripes of various widths corresponding to the different visual acuity levels. The targets are presented simultaneously and the narrowest lines the child views preferentially correlate to his visual acuity.

For those children between the ages of two-and-a-half and five, picture charts may be used to evaluate visual acuity. You may want to ask your doctor if he or she will allow your child to become familiar with the images before the test because your child will not be able to identify images he doesn't recognize, like that of a rotary phone. You don't want his inability to name the image to be mistaken for a lack of acuity.

For anyone old enough to know the alphabet, the most common tool for measuring visual acuity is the standard Snellen chart. The examiner places the chart twenty feet from the child and asks him to read the letters. Visual acuity is assessed by determining the smallest line of letters the child can see clearly. The Snellen measurement is recorded as a fraction, such as 20/20 or 20/200. The numerator (or upper number) is usually recorded as the individual's distance from the chart. The denominator (or lower number) refers to the relative size of the letter or character. In this example, the smallest letter viewed clearly by someone with 20/200 vision is ten times larger than the one viewed clearly by someone with 20/20 vision.

However, the Snellen chart does not provide enough gradations to accurately diagnose an individual with low vision. The Snellen measurements go from 20/100 to 20/200 to 20/400. So a child who has 20/160 vision would most likely be categorized as 20/200, and over-prescribed. As a result, low vision charts were developed to address this problem. These charts usually have more letters of each size, and the size increments are smaller. These charts come with letters, pictures and tumbling E's for use with children of different ages and literacy levels. Low vision charts give a more realistic measure of acuity for those with albinism because they offer a more precise assessment of what size letter or object a person sees clearly.

One common low vision chart is called the LogMAR. Many ophthalmologists find this type of chart too complicated to use in their general practice and are thus unfamiliar with it. If possible, seek out a practitioner who has experience with low vision individuals and low vision charts. The more accurate the measurement of your child's visual acuity, the more precisely his vision can be corrected, which will increase the quality of the information reaching his brain.

Refractive Error: Types and Measurement

The term refractive error refers to myopia (nearsightedness), hyperopia (farsightedness) and astigmatism (blurred vision). These disorders of the eye are routinely treated with glasses or contact lenses, and the result is that the retina receives a focused image. However, because people with albinism have genetic differences in their retina and optic nerve, getting the best image to the retina does not result in completely corrected vision. In other words, corrected acuity means the best visual acuity that the particular individual with albinism can obtain. The goal is still to get the best image to the retina, so lenses can help people with albinism see better, even though they do not see 20/20. Treating refractive error in babies and young children is important because better images going to the retina and optic nerve mean better information going to the brain.

Hyperopia, or farsightedness, is a common condition in which people see distant objects more clearly than close objects. It occurs when the eyeball is too short for light rays to properly focus on the retina, so an image appears blurred. If left uncorrected this can cause significant eye strain and reduced performance and stamina. However, the use of corrective lenses may provide little actual improvement in visual acuity. Farsightedness is extremely common in those with albinism.

Astigmatism is a condition caused when the cornea is not "perfectly" round. If left uncorrected by eyeglasses or contact lenses, it may result in blurred vision. Most people with albinism have a significant degree of astigmatism.

Myopia, or nearsightedness, results from the eye being too long or the refractive power of the cornea and lens of the eye being too strong, so images are formed in front of the retina and appear blurred. People with myopia may read and see close objects more clearly with their glasses off.

Your child's refractive error can be determined both objectively and subjectively. A doctor will usually start with an objective measurement, particularly with very young children who cannot communicate effectively. A hand-held instrument called a retinoscope is used to reflect a beam of light from the retina. The doctor observes the movement of that reflected beam of light and tries different lenses to neutralize, or correct, that movement. While this can be done without dilating the eyes, a better result may occur if the eyes have been dilated. Another objective test of refraction is called auto-refraction. In this test, the child looks at a target

Photo courtesy of Positive Exposure, Rick Guidotti

within the instrument while a low level infrared beam scans the retina and a computer analyses the movement of the reflected beam. This can be used for children starting at age two or three. The eye movement due to the nystagmus makes this testing slightly more difficult.

When your child is older, his input will be an important part of the exam. Subjective refraction relies on the patient to determine the lens that results in the best visual acuity at a test distance of ten or twenty feet. This testing often includes questions from the examiner such as, "Which is better, one or two?" or "Tell me when the letters get worse." Even though this testing can be tedious and the individual may lack confidence in his responses, the results can be remarkably accurate. An experienced optometrist or ophthalmologist will listen to the tone of the patient's voice and watch body language while testing to achieve accurate results.

Refractive testing should also include testing of near-point vision. This is especially important when your child begins to read. People with albinism hold printed material very close to read, and often have a different lens prescription for reading. As a result, your child may have bifocals or a specific pair of reading glasses.

Additional Tests

Your doctor may also use additional tests if the standard tests are ambiguous or unclear. These can include visual evoked potential (VEP) and nystagmography.

VEP is an electro-diagnostic test that can record the brain wave patterns in the visual cortex of the brain. It is used to estimate visual acuity and determine any "miswiring" of the visual pathway from the eyes to the part of the brain that interprets visual input. This procedure involves placing electrodes on the back of the head over the visual cortex to measure the brain's response to different patterns of flashing lights. This test can be used to rule out albinism, if certain patterns are not observed.

A nystagmograph is an instrument that records eye movements. In particular, it helps identify the speed and amount of nystagmus movement. An individual may display significantly different nystagmus patterns when he gazes in different directions, focuses on different distances and experiences different levels of fatigue and concentration. Because of the variability of the rate of nystagmus, these recordings have minimal clinical significance but can be useful in laboratory studies.

Your child should also be tested for any color vision anomalies, because people with albinism rely heavily on color to identify objects in their daily lives. Children need to know their numbers and be able to make color judgments to complete this test. Typically, children must be five to six years old before their color vision can be tested reliably.

The Low vision Exam

A low vision examination differs from a general eye examination because much of the testing is designed to evaluate different aspects of visual function. A low vision exam will use many of the same evaluation techniques as a regular eye exam, such as a detailed medical history and an assessment of refractive error. However, the low vision specialist will focus on improving visual function through the use of devices and adaptive skills. As described above, the doctor will use different charts and tools designed for low vision individuals.

The emphasis is on how your child sees in the real world, and how best to maximize visual function. Once again, it is not how much vision your child has, but how he uses the vision he has that is important. Low vision specialists seek to train individuals to use their vision for maximum effectiveness.

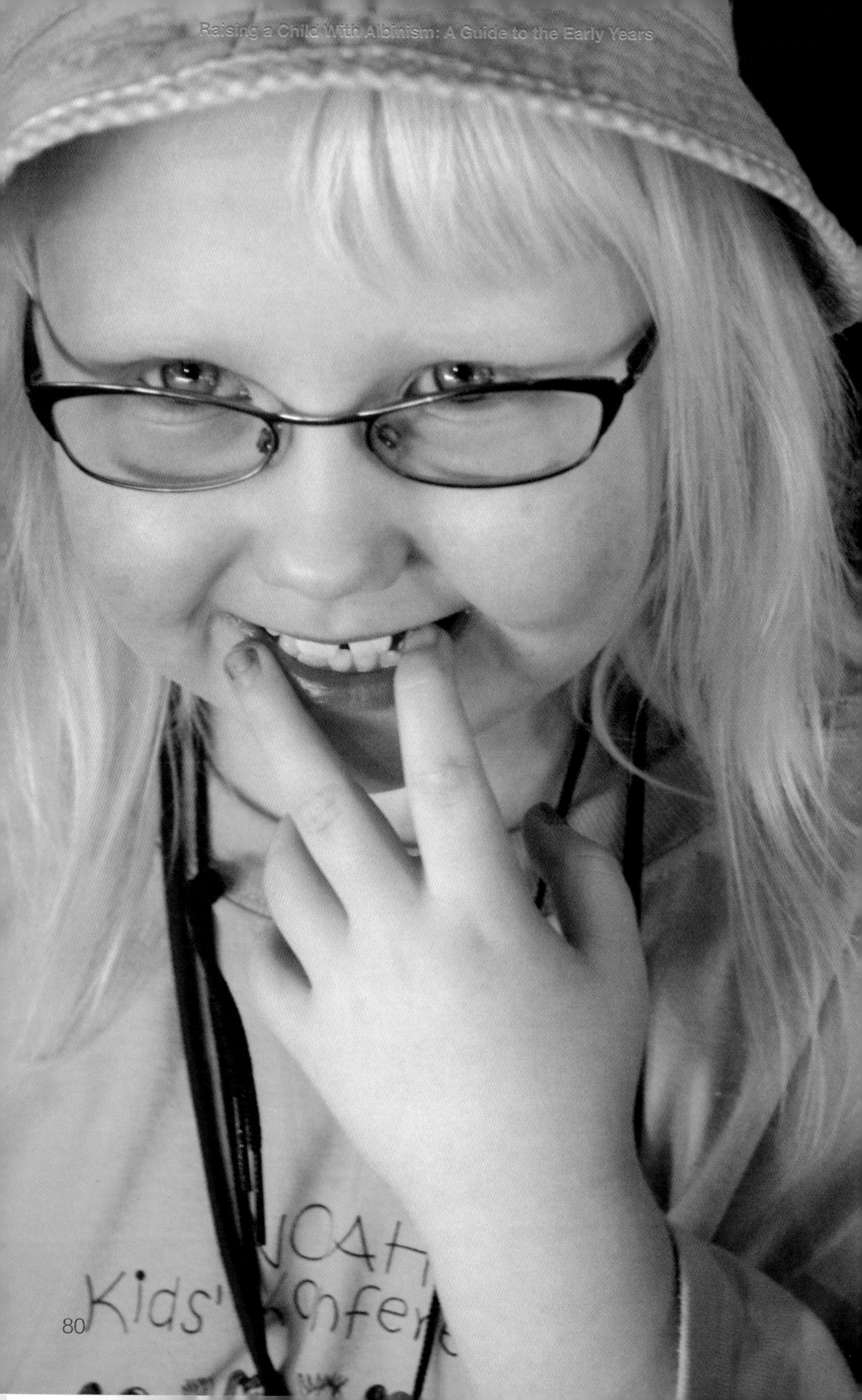
Kids'

Chapter 6

Treatment Options

A number of treatment options are available to improve the functional vision of children with albinism. These include eyeglasses, sunglasses, contact lenses, low vision devices, vision therapy and surgery. This chapter offers a brief overview of these options, to help you make an informed decision when you consult with your eye care professional about the right choice for your child.

Eyeglasses

People with albinism almost always develop significant refractive errors in their eyesight, including a substantial amount of astigmatism, usually in combination with hyperopia (farsightedness) and myopia (nearsighted-ness). These refractive errors generally appear early in the child's life, typically between six months and three years of age.

Many parents wonder when to get the first pair of eyeglasses for their child with albinism. While there are no clear guidelines on when to prescribe the first pair of corrective lenses, different doctors suggest different approaches. Some doctors advise parents to "wait and see," preferring not to prescribe glasses until a child goes to school. Other medical professionals believe it is important to correct a child's vision as early as possible – even within the first few months of life. They believe that the better the image received by the brain, the better vision will develop.

In addition to improving visual acuity, prescription eyeglasses offer a number of other benefits to children with albinism. Wearing eyeglasses can substantially improve comfort and concentration for children when they're looking at books, reading or watching television. Wearing eyeglasses can also lessen the involuntary eye movements of nystagmus and the strabismus that causes the eyes to move out of unison. Amblyopia may also be prevented in many cases. If possible, it is best that your child wear her eyeglasses at all times. Another practical consideration is that a child who becomes accustomed to wearing eyeglasses as a toddler, may not resist them when she reaches school age.

If your child has difficulty keeping the eyeglasses on, do not make it a battle. Stop for a few days and try again. It is sometimes easier to get your child to wear the eyeglasses if you slip them on her while she is engaged in perusing a book or playing with a toy. Some children's frames have cable temples which wrap under the ear, or a head strap that holds the frame snugly in place. In most cases, the improved vision provides enough of an incentive to keep the eyeglasses on – once the habit has been formed. If your child consistently refuses to wear the glasses, check the fit, the comfort of the frame and the accuracy of the lens prescription. Children often can't articulate what exactly is bothering them about the glasses.

If you or your spouse wears eyeglasses, make putting them on, cleaning them and caring for them a family affair. You can allow a two-year-old to "help" you take care of his glasses, and make it seem like a big, important job. For very young children, you can play a game of "peek-a-boo" while putting on the glasses.

Tinted prescription lenses can also be helpful for children with albinism, to reduce glare and light sensitivity. A slight blue tint can make classroom lighting less harsh, and many families opt for photochromic or transition lenses that darken automatically when the ambient light gets brighter.

Contact Lenses

People with albinism may choose to wear contact lenses for a variety of reasons. For some older children and adults, contact lenses can be desirable for cosmetic reasons, while others find eyeglasses inconvenient for playing sports. Some people report that they get better visual acuity and reduced nystagmus by wearing contact lenses. There are also many people who wear both contact lenses and their regular prescription glasses, finding that the combination gives them the best acuity.

The decision to prescribe contact lenses should be made with your child's ophthalmologist, and will depend on your child's age, maturity and level of responsibility. Generally speaking, contact lenses can be prescribed when your child is responsible enough to care for them. However, some ophthalmologists prefer to wait until the late teen years because the risk of developing an allergy to the lens material is much less then.

Contact lenses can also be a useful tool to reduce light-sensitivity, or photophobia. The lenses can be ordered with a prescription and a tint that helps reduce unwanted light from entering the eye. If your child is especially photophobic, tinted contact lenses can make a big difference. Because the technology changes rapidly, you should discuss the option with your child's doctor when the time is right.

Photo courtesy of Positive Exposure, Rick Guidotti

Surgery

Many parents question whether surgery can help improve their child's vision. Surgery won't "fix" low vision, but it can help with some of the vision problems associated with albinism. The decision to seek surgery for your child is personal, and because of the risks involved, it must be well researched. Surgical options and opinions vary, and the field advances all the time.

The most common surgery for people with albinism is strabismus surgery. This procedure is most often performed to improve appearance by aligning the eyes. It may also help prevent vision loss by encouraging use of the weaker eye. Strabismus surgery usually involves either recessing, or resecting one or more of the eye muscles.

Nystagmus surgery, called tenotomy, is typically performed if a person's null point is off center. The null point is the direction the eyes are looking where the nystagmus is at a minimum or has stopped. For many people with albinism, the null point is off center, so they achieve their best vision when they tilt their head to one side or up or down.

The nystagmus surgery also requires recession or resection of selected extra-ocular muscles to move the null point so the nystagmus movement is at its minimum while the person is looking straight ahead. The goal is improved appearance, and a slight improvement of visual acuity. As with any surgery, there is always risk involved, and you are encouraged to seek at least two opinions as to whether it will benefit your child.

Patching

Children with strabismus or amblyopia may wear an eye patch to help treat the deficit, and those who experience a large difference in refractive error between the two eyes may also wear an eye patch to lessen the difference. In these situations, the patch is worn on the good eye. Patching is the most common method for reducing strabismus, which, if left untreated, can result in amblyopia and permanent vision loss. Your doctor will recommend the length and duration of a patch regimen, based on your child's particular symptoms.

To maximize the impact of patching, it is very important to do it regularly. As with any muscle, the eye will respond to regular exercise by becoming stronger. There are several things you can do to encourage your child to cooperate:

- Allow your child to watch a favorite television program while wearing the patch.
- Give your child control over a kid-friendly timer so she has the important job of monitoring the time limit.
- Be creative with the patch. Draw a skull and crossbones on it so your child can be a pirate, or add a "magic eye" or a cat's eye. Let your child select and help decorate the patch.

When using the traditional "pirate type" patch on children with albinism, nystagmus may increase, which often negates any help the patch may offer. If your child has a noticeable increase in nystagmus, discuss the use of a dilating eye drop called atropine with your doctor. This might also be an effective alternative if your child resists wearing a patch. The use of atropine has recently been shown to be more effective than the traditional patch in reducing amblyopia. The eye drop is used in the good eye, thus dilating the pupil and paralyzing the ciliary muscle. Since the individual cannot focus with the good eye due to the significant blur, her weak eye is forced to work harder. Over a period of time, this should reduce the amblyopia, but will not reduce the need for eyeglasses.

Vision Therapy

Vision therapy is a term that describes a number of procedures that stimulate vision and enhance visual skills. Some optometrists – usually developmental optometrists – offer vision therapy, but it can be difficult to obtain because of a lack of providers and a lack of willingness on the part of insurers to cover it. Therefore, much of the focus of this book is to teach parents simple techniques they can use themselves on a daily basis.

Vision therapy uses a variety of measures to integrate the senses of balance, touch and "proprioception," which is the sense one has of one's own body. The term "sensory integration" refers to the way we use these internal and external senses together. It also refers to the way muscles (including those involved in fine motor and gross motor movement, speech and oculomotor, or eye movement, must work in harmony with all of the senses, including sight. Because low vision has an impact on the other senses and their ability to work together, it is important to teach your child the techniques necessary to increase visual reach and coordination. Simple games, as well as household chores and tasks, are great tools for creating your own vision therapy program and increasing your child's visual reach.

Photo courtesy of Positive Exposure, Rick Guidotti

Chapter 7

Service Providers

This chapter explains the various service providers who are available to help your child adapt to the unique requirements of living with albinism. Among these service providers are the teacher of the visually impaired (TVI), the Certified Orientation and Mobility Specialist (COMS) and the occupational therapist (OT). In some areas of the country a TVI may be hard to find, due to a national shortage. If that is the case where you live, don't panic. Advocate strongly for your jurisdiction to find a TVI, and work with an orientation and mobility specialist or an OT, until one is hired. These specialists can be valuable providers, particularly with your guidance.

In most cases, you will be a successful advocate for the services your child needs, and state or school officials will offer appropriate services to address your child's visual impairment. In other cases you may meet with resistance. If you are having difficulty obtaining services, connect with others in the albinism and visually impaired communities. Ask what suggestions and resources they have to help you and your child.

Accept the services that your early intervention program or school district offers. Occupational and physical therapists, along with early childhood specialists, can provide some great assistance to your child. You will need to work closely with these individuals if they do not have experience or extensive knowledge of albinism or visual impairments. In addition, there is excellent material on the NOAH website for educators

Photo courtesy of Mashawna Thompson

and service providers. Adapt this material to fit your child's particular needs, and always reach out to others in the albinism community with questions and concerns.

Teacher of the Visually Impaired (TVI)

A teacher of the visually impaired (TVI) is a certified teacher with additional certification to work with the visually impaired. A TVI can teach your child strategies to help him accommodate everyday tasks for his visual impairment. A TVI provides assessment, information and advice for educational planning, and will collaborate with you and your child's teachers to ensure that your child has access to all information and experiences in his environment. The following are basic duties a TVI may perform for a child with albinism.

Conduct a Functional Vision Assessment (FVA)

A functional vision assessment (FVA) is a comprehensive evaluation of a child's needs. It is used to ensure that material is presented in a way that best meets your child's visual needs, and that the proper lighting, seating, reading and writing tools are in place. This evaluation should be done by a teacher certified in the area of visual impairments and/or a COMS. It is done at the time of referral for vision-related services and may be repeated at any time as needed. The FVA provides more detailed information about how your child sees and how his vision affects his functioning in daily life. Even young infants can have a FVA.

A young child's FVA might include assessment in several areas with different objects. The lighting in the room and the distance of the objects will be varied to get an accurate picture of your child's vision. It should be conducted at different times of the day, and in any place your child will be expected to learn. Your child will also be evaluated on the following:

- Glare sensitivity
- Light preference
- Best placement for items such as on a raised platform or slanted board
- Object/letter size preference and distance child needs to be from certain items
- Hand-eye coordination
- Peripheral vision
- Scanning the environment
- Locating, fixating, tracking and following an object

A school-age child will be assessed in the same areas, but additional factors will be included, such as optimal seating in a classroom, most effective writing utensil and the use of adaptive devices. Using the results of the FVA, the TVI will recommend accommodations to meet your child's visual needs and allow him to use his vision most effectively. This report will be shared with other service providers, teachers and caregivers, so they know how your child sees and what conditions are ideal for his visual functioning.

The TVI will also be an important part of the committee that will determine whether your child meets the criteria as a student with a visual impairment and is therefore eligible for services. A TVI may work on a "monitor consult" basis, checking in with your child periodically, or may work more intensively with your child, meeting on a regular daily, weekly, bi-weekly or monthly basis. You may hear that an "itinerant teacher of the visually impaired" serves your child. This means the teacher travels to your child's school or home for services. If your child must travel to a TVI, his arrangement may go by a variety of terms, such as resource program or center-based service.

Many children with albinism are educated in a general education school setting with some support services to accommodate the visual impairment. However, it is not uncommon for additional services to be added to help your child "catch up" if needed. Service providers may suggest that you place your child in a special education pre-school to give him a little extra support. Please see the section "Your Child in the Classroom" for more information on this option.

Adaptations and Accommodations

After the results of the FVA are incorporated into the IEP, the TVI's major responsibility is to implement and monitor the accommodations and strategies that will give your child access to the educational curriculum. These may include:

- Adaptation of materials in alternative formats, such as large print or audio format.
- Training in the use of low vision devices (magnifiers, monoculars, video magnifiers).
- Introduction of slant boards or raised platforms for close-up work.
- Monitoring lighting and changes in the physical environment to make your child more comfortable and better able to function.
- Identifying methods and devices to increase the contrast on a page and decrease the glare on a surface.
- Ordering adaptive materials for your child's school and for testing. These may include large print or audio books and adaptive devices to use at school.

Photo courtesy of Positive Exposure, Rick Guidotti

Instruction

A TVI will also work one-on-one with your child to help him develop skills and accommodative strategies. Instruction may focus on:

- Visual stimulation and the development of visual efficiency skills.
- General child development skills, including motor skills, concept development and communication. The TVI may implement visual adaptations to help your child in these areas.
- Literacy, including the use of large print or audio books and other methods to encourage an interest in books, reading and writing.
- Enhancing compensatory skills so your child can use other senses or methods to compensate for his visual impairment.
- Use of low vision devices, adaptive computer programs or other items that accommodate your child's visual impairment.
- Recreation, leisure and social skill support and adaptations.

Academic and Social Support

A TVI will also help your child learn how to talk about his visual impairment and albinism. This may include discussing ways to ask for assistance or accommodations, how to answer questions about albinism and how to identify and appropriately deal with harassment, discrimination and bullying. A TVI may also engage in role-playing to build problem-solving skills and methods to help your child become independent and able to self-accommodate vision-related needs.

Since some children with visual impairments miss certain concepts presented visually in class – such as handwriting instruction conducted on the chalkboard – a TVI may reinforce school lessons to make sure your child does not have gaps in his academic learning. Your child may also benefit from learning certain skills directly from a TVI, such as how to touch-type. Many children with visual impairments benefit from learning and perfecting this skill before their sighted peers.

Will my child learn Braille?

The need to learn Braille is based on each child's own visual condition and individual literacy needs. Most people with albinism do not learn Braille because they have enough useable, functional vision not to need Braille. However, if your child has particularly low vision that limits access to print, a TVI may discuss Braille instruction.

Certified Orientation and Mobility Specialist

Orientation and Mobility (O&M) services are designed to offer safe options for independent travel in everyday life for people who are blind or visually impaired. Although you may think independent travel is a long way off for your child, even during infancy, children learn about their environment, direction and spatial relations that lead to independent travel in the years to come.

A Certified Orientation and Mobility Specialist (COMS) is trained to help people with visual impairments travel through the environment safely, effectively and independently. Children with albinism typically have relatively good functional vision and often do not need mobility services. However, O&M skills are important to help your child compensate for his low vision, and will help him learn to negotiate the world with confidence.

> " I had mobility training before entering each school in Medfield. I would definitely recommend this. My mobility specialist would give me a tour of the new school and show me tips and ways to make my way around without getting lost. I often found myself giving directions to my peers on the first day of school. I felt comfortable in the new environment and didn't have to worry about getting lost! "
>
> Kristen Daley
> Medfield, MA
> young adult with albinism

Working with your child in the toddler and pre-school years, a COMS can help enhance motor development, balance and posture; can help you identify environmental factors that may affect the safety of your child when he is learning to walk or crawl; and can help you identify resources and activities to explore with your child. When your child enters school, a COMS can assist in route-planning techniques, safe street-crossing methods, and strategies for dealing with the school environment.

A mobility specialist can also help you and your child select and use low vision aids, such as monoculars, and sun filters. In addition, a mobility specialist can help you understand what your child sees when traveling outdoors. For example, when planning a bike trip, a mobility specialist can help identify terrains that are difficult for your child to see, such as changes in pavement, tree roots, overhanging branches and rocks. Also, biking through an area that changes in contrast and brightness may be difficult for people with albinism. A mobility specialist can provide techniques for you to use to minimize the impact of glare, shade-to-sun transitions or unfamiliar terrain.

Not all children with albinism need help from an O&M specialist, but if your child is having difficulty safely navigating new environments, if he trips a lot on steps or other obstacles, or if you have other concerns, inquire about having your child assessed by a mobility specialist. If there are none in your area, discuss your concerns with your pediatrician or with an occupational therapist.

Occupational Therapist

An occupational therapist (OT) can be a great resource for a child with albinism. This is particularly true when a TVI is not available. While some children with albinism exhibit a short delay in reaching developmental milestones, some also have a fear of falling, of sudden noises and of new textures. OTs can help because it focuses on the child's gross and fine motor skills, oral motor functioning, feeding, social skills and sensory processing.

The therapist will develop non-visual stimuli and activities to build compensatory skills, and help your child gain confidence in his movements and his environment. An OT will probably not have much experience with a child with albinism, so it is important to provide him or her with a written explanation of albinism and how it affects your child. Occupational therapists can adjust everyday tasks and help modify your child's environment to suit his particular needs. The OT can suggest lighting adaptations to address low vision; sensory substitution, including audiotapes and special talking devices; computer technology; adaptive writing materials; tactile markings and other adaptations.

Photo courtesy of Positive Exposure, Rick Guidotti

Chapter 8

Early Intervention Services

The world of special education services is full of confusing acronyms and legal phrases. In an attempt to demystify the process, this chapter outlines the basic services that many children with albinism receive at some point in their development.

The Individuals with Disabilities Education Act (IDEA) is a federal law mandating that all children with disabilities are entitled to a free, appropriate public education that includes special education and related services designed to meet their unique needs and to prepare them for employment and independent living. It provides funds to assist states in the education of students with disabilities and requires that states protect the rights of children with disabilities and their parents. Children with a visual impairment are eligible for services under IDEA from birth through the age of twenty-one.

For children under the age of three, IDEA assists states in providing early intervention services (EIS) under a program called the Individualized Family Service Plan (IFSP). For children age three to twenty-one, these services are provided after an evaluation and the development of a written, legal document called the Individualized Education Program (IEP).

The United States Department of Education website contains all the information you need as a parent of a child with a visual impairment to familiarize yourself with IDEA – the federal law that provides special education for children with disabilities. The website site is **http://idea. ed.gov**.

Early Intervention and Assessments

A child with albinism will often have short delays in development resulting from low vision. Fine motor skills, such as grasping small objects, and gross motor skills, such as walking, may come more slowly. Understanding early intervention services is an important part of meeting your child's developmental needs. Not all children with albinism will need these services, but it is important to have a clear understanding of how to get help if your child needs it.

Early intervention services (EIS) is the name of a national program that provides individual care to infants and toddlers in the United States who have conditions that affect their development or their senses, including vision. Children with albinism should qualify for EIS because albinism impairs sight. Sight is an important factor in most areas of development, so early intervention for children with albinism may include the services of a TVI or other services such as physical therapy (PT) or occupational therapy (OT) for motor skills, speech therapy, or O&M training. You can get a referral for early intervention services from your pediatrician. It is a good idea to register your child with your state EIS office even if you do not see a measurable developmental delay. By registering for these services, you can meet with a TVI or other specialist who can provide you with additional strategies to help keep your child's development on track. It will also provide you with a contact point in case you have a question or concern about your child.

When parents contact the EIS agency in their state, the local EIS provider should make an appointment to meet with the parent(s) or guardian and the child. The meeting usually takes place in the home. The EIS representative should ask for information about the child, family, and medical diagnosis or treatment, and should evaluate the child by watching and interacting or playing with him. It is helpful to give the EIS representative a copy of medical records from the doctor who diagnosed the albinism. Because not all EIS representatives will be familiar with albinism, you should also prepare a short written statement explaining albinism and how it may affect your child. Outline the vision issues and explain photophobia, nystagmus and null point. Describe how they may impact vision and development. Clearly explain any concerns you are having, and whether you think low vision is a contributing factor. It is important to provide this information to the service provider so that he or she can accurately assess your child's development.

Evaluation and Testing

An EIS representative will assess your child's level of functioning in cognitive, fine motor, gross motor and social, visual and self-help skills. Results are used to determine eligibility for special education services, and to identify the presence of disabilities in addition to the visual impairment. If, for any reason, the EIS representative does not qualify and enroll your child in EIS after the initial appointment, you may wish to follow up with the diagnosing doctor or see another medical specialist to get a more thorough report on vision impairment. You have the right to request another EIS evaluation at any time to reconsider enrollment or to reconsider the kind of services the child receives once enrolled in the program.

Certain factors must be considered when testing a child with a visual impairment. Professionals who examine your child may not have experience with visual impairment and may not be familiar with low vision accommodations. It is important to provide the specialist with background information on albinism, and for you to advocate for appropriate accommodations for your child so the evaluation can be as valid as possible. Remember to consider the following environmental factors:

- Is the material presented in a way that your child can access it? Can she get close enough to the image to see it?
- Is the test room "albinism-friendly?" Is there glare coming in from outside windows? Are there harsh fluorescent lights and blinding white walls?
- Does the testing surface promote good contrast? If your baby will be tested on the floor, can a dark, solid-color blanket be used to eliminate glare and help with contrast?

While you want to make your child comfortable, it is also important for the evaluator to recognize and perhaps observe the difficulties your child may have with glare and mobility.

A Word About Evaluations and Assessments

During infancy and early childhood it may be difficult to determine if a child with a visual impairment has any other impairments of concern. Professionals who have little or no experience with children with a visual impairment may attribute learning delays, particularly in the area of reading, to the child's low vision, when there is actually a second disability that warrants attention. Some go the opposite direction and demand that you have your child tested for all sorts of disabilities when the only problem is the visual impairment. Yet others may attribute any developmental delays to personality traits such as laziness. For example, an evaluator may conclude that a child does not read for long periods of time because she is lazy, when the real reason is that the child's eyes and neck fatigue quickly so she rests periodically during reading time. Whichever circumstance you find yourself in, remember that no test or professional can give a completely accurate depiction of your child's abilities and needs.

Assessment Recommendations

After your child has been evaluated, the EIS representative may recommend services to address your child's needs. Among the possibilities are low vision services, physical therapy, occupational therapy or speech therapy. Some parents welcome the help they will receive, while others are concerned about their child being placed in "special education" even during early infancy. All services for children with disabilities are there to help. Many minor problems that begin during early infancy can be proactively handled with proper services so they do not escalate and cause the child to fall farther behind. The United States Department of Education reports that early intervention increases children's developmental and educational gains, improves the functioning of their family, and creates long-term benefits for society. Studies show that children who receive early intervention services need fewer special education and other habilitative services later in life, are held a second year in the same grade less often, and in some cases are indistinguishable from non-handicapped classmates years after intervention.

Another positive aspect of early intervention is that your child's service provider will observe and work with your child on a continuing basis, which allows for a highly reliable assessment of his visual impairment. Assessments administered in a single day are much less reliable, as your child may have been tired, sick, shy, or just not in the mood for a test. A

Photo courtesy of Susan Leslie DuBois

specialist who meets with your child on a regular basis can monitor your child's progress and observe her in a variety of situations. Your child will become familiar with the service provider and may be more relaxed and natural, demonstrating her true abilities and impairments.

Individualized Family Service Plan

After evaluation and at the time of enrollment, the EIS representative will propose an Individual Family Service Plan (IFSP) when the child is under the age of three. The IFSP is a very important document – a record of the service plan created for your child. It will outline the types, frequency and location of services to be provided, the goals the child should reach, and the parent or guardian's agreement to make the child available for EIS appointments and to take the necessary steps to put the IFSP into action.

The IFSP is a contract that requires the consent of the child's parent or guardian. Before signing the ISFP, a parent or guardian may request that it be modified to include more or less frequent services than initially recommended, or may request different services than those proposed by the EIS evaluator. Parents and guardians may also ask other people, such as a doctor, nurse or teacher, to participate in developing the IFSP before it is signed. Once the parent or guardian agrees to and signs the IFSP, it must then be reviewed and updated at least once a year. Nonetheless, a parent or guardian may request re-evaluation to change or adjust the plan at any time.

Because an IFSP is an individual plan, it is impossible to list what should or should not be included for every child with albinism. Each child is different, particularly in terms of sight, vision development, and any effects vision may have on other skills and development. However, services for infants and toddlers with albinism will usually include regular visits, once a week or so, by a TVI.

Goals may include reaching certain developmental milestones, stimulating vision development through regular therapy with the TVI, adaptations in the home and/or daycare environment to improve visual surroundings, and making parents, guardians and other primary caregivers aware of the child's vision needs and how best to meet those needs and stimulate vision development. In addition to vision goals, the IFSP will also include goals for gross motor and fine motor skill development, if delays in those areas are found. You may also want to include socialization goals – for example, encouraging and measuring your child's ability to make and maintain appropriate eye contact.

A good relationship with EIS providers is important, because they can be a great source of helpful information and assistance, especially when children transition from EIS to school after age three. However, if parents or guardians become dissatisfied with services or progress, or cannot reach agreement with the EIS provider about the contents of what should be in the IFSP, there may be administrative and legal options available under the IDEA, the federal law that governs the EIS program. Legal and administrative options are usually limited to reimbursement, obtaining services or obtaining re-evaluation of an IFSP if a request is not honored. There are also parent advocacy groups in each state to provide information, workshops and assistance to families with IFSPs.

Individualized Education Program

As the parent of a child with albinism, you will encounter many unfamiliar terms and acronyms. Among the most important is Individualized Education Program, commonly referred to as an IEP. This is a written document developed for each child three years and older who will attend public school and who is eligible for special education. It is a detailed plan that outlines the accommodations and education goals your child needs to fully access all aspects of a public school education. Special education is a set of services, rather than a specific place for your child to go. Most children with albinism do very well in a general education setting when certain accommodations or modifications to classroom materials are made.

While the IDEA is the federal law that creates the right to special education services, each state has its own interpretation of this law via state-specific special education laws and regulations. For more information about these rights in your area, contact your local school district's department of special education or your state department of special education. You can find more information in the Resources Section of this book.

A good resource is Wrightslaw, a website that has up-to-date information about special education law, education law and advocacy for children with disabilities. See their website at **www.wrightslaw.com.**

Under the IDEA, your child is eligible for special education services at no cost to you if she is a child with a disability and if she requires special education and related services to benefit from the general education program. This means an evaluation has determined that without accommodations, she will not have equal access to an education.

The process for creating an IEP should start after your child turns three, whether or not she is in a pre-school environment. By the time your child reaches kindergarten, you should have worked with your local school district or state office to create an IFSP. If not, contact your state department of special education at least six months before your child is scheduled to enter kindergarten to begin the process.

It is important to remember that while most educators truly work in the best interest of the child, most are unfamiliar with albinism and can mistakenly under-assess the need for accommodations because our children are as bright as all the rest and are highly adaptable. You are the expert in your child's development and must follow your instincts if you believe services are warranted.

Ask lots of questions, and don't be embarrassed if you are unfamiliar with the jargon used at these education meetings. Many of the acronyms and terms are specific to special education and are not widely known. The following discussion of the IEP process includes strategies for getting the services your child needs.

Photo courtesy of Positive Exposure, Rick Guidotti

Eligibility

Children with albinism are generally entitled to an IEP on the basis of the diagnosis alone, since it almost always includes a significant visual impairment. Your child does not need to be "legally blind" to qualify for services, but you will need to provide a recent ophthalmologic report, and your child will have to be evaluated by the local public school district. It is a good idea to create a written request for evaluation, and address it to the school principal or the district's special education coordinator. This written request should include a description of your child, the impact of albinism on his vision and development, and any reports from doctors or other service providers that illustrate your concerns. You should be very specific, and outline the direct impact of your child's visual impairment and/or photophobia. The following is an example of an evaluation request for a four-year-old child:

"The purpose of this letter is to request a special education evaluation for our son. Tommy has albinism, which is a genetic condition that results in a lack of pigment in his eyes and skin. Please find copies of his most recent medical and ophthalmologic evaluations, as well as a statement from his pediatrician. Our concerns are based on the following:

- Tommy is visually impaired and cannot identify letters written on a blackboard unless he is within six inches. He must hold a book very close to his face to see the pictures and words, and cannot see artwork or materials hung high on the wall.
- Bright lights hurt Tommy's eyes, and when a room is too bright, he will squint or close his eyes. As a result, he misses much of what is going on around him.
- Tommy has trouble making and maintaining eye contact, and noticing facial expressions and non-verbal communication because of his visual impairment. As a result, he has a difficult time making friends.

We are requesting an evaluation to determine Tommy's strengths and weaknesses, and to identify what accommodations are necessary to help him succeed in the school setting."

The most important thing to communicate is your request for an evaluation. Do not offer suggestions for potential services or accommodations. It is more difficult to deny a request for an evaluation than it is to deny a direct appeal for services. You should receive a written response to your request that proposes an evaluation plan or details why an evaluation is being denied. You should also receive a copy of your legal rights and responsibilities, which you are strongly encouraged to read, and keep for your records. An evaluation cannot take place until you provide written consent. Once the school receives your consent, state-mandated timelines begin to run and the school is required to take action.

If you have been denied an evaluation, you have the right to appeal the decision. You may want to seek additional statements from your child's doctor and contact NOAH for assistance in appealing the decision. It is a good idea to be very familiar with your rights under state law. You may want to get the name of a lawyer who specializes in IDEA and education law, so that you have a resource to fall back on. Having this information can be very persuasive when trying to convince the local school district to reassess your child's eligibility.

> When I've had issues with my son's services, I've always written letters. I tend to quote parts of the IDEA or items from the "state parental rights" booklet to show them that I am not some meek and mild parent who can be pushed around. You have to establish yourself as being knowledgeable about your son's rights under the law.
>
> As a parent, you need to actively advocate for your son and not let up on the pressure to get the services that [the school] already agreed to provide by signing off on the IEP. I have kept the name and address of a disability rights lawyer in my son's file, just in case things get to the point where I feel I need to go that route.
>
> Jeannine Stearns
> Boxborough, MA
> parent of a child with albinism

Creating the IEP

Once your child has been deemed eligible to receive services, you will help to create an IEP through a team effort with educators and administrators. It will be reviewed at least once a year. As the parent, you are an invaluable part of the IEP team because you know your child best and are most aware of the impact of albinism on his development. The other members of the multidisciplinary team can include a general education teacher, a special education teacher and a representative of the school district who knows about the services available and has the authority to commit resources. If your child has a vision teacher, it is very important that he or she participate too.

You have the right to request that other individuals be present at the meeting, and you should include anyone you feel can offer insight. For example, you may want to include an occupational therapist if you are concerned about your child's motor development, or if he has received therapy services. If there is no vision specialist available, you may want to ask a representative from your state office for the blind and visually impaired to accompany you, or perhaps there is another NOAH parent in the area who can provide you with support.

Many IEPs are created at the end of the school year in a very rushed manner, as schools must complete all IEPs within a certain time frame. Try and schedule your meeting early, and if you feel that you are being rushed, ask to schedule another meeting to fully address all your concerns.

The IEP must contain information about your child's strengths and needs, as identified by you, by his teachers (if applicable) and by the school staff who evaluated him. Observations and results of the special education evaluation, including individually administered standardized tests, are reviewed. In addition to academic skills, the team must consider language development, behavior and social skills, other nonacademic skills and any pertinent assistive technology. This is when you want to be fully prepared to explain the impact of albinism on your child's daily life. For example, one parent routinely borrows from the state office for the blind a pair of low vision goggles that simulate her daughter's level of impairment to give the IEP team first-hand experience in being in a class-room with 20/200 vision. This current set of circumstances is referred to as your child's "present level of performance" – inelegantly called "plops" for short. It is used to develop a complete picture of your child and to fully understand the impact of her disability on her performance.

After the IEP team discusses everyone's observations and comments, the next step is to create measurable goals that your child can reasonably accomplish in one year. The goals are based on your child's "plops," and must directly relate to the needs that result from the disability. The IDEA states that a child's IEP must include "a description of how the child's progress toward the annual goals... will be measured and when periodic reports on the progress the child is making toward annual goals will be provided." The following are two goals and their measurements from an IEP for a kindergartner with albinism:

Goal: By X date (usually one year hence), Tommy will develop strategies (such as scanning, appreciating contrast, noticing visual cues) for finding objects on a page and in his environment that will enable him to access the curriculum presented in class and to play with peers on nine out of ten trials.

Goal: By X date (usually one year hence), Tommy will request needed accommodations and/or utilize adaptive strategies in order to access classroom materials and actively participate in classroom activities, given one verbal prompt, four out of five times.

The IEP will also detail the accommodations or modifications necessary to help your child fully participate in the general education setting. When identifying goals and accommodations, be prepared with a checklist of issues that you want to make sure are covered. The list of issues will be different for each child, but should always address how to make the written material accessible for your child.

Typical accommodations for children with albinism include worksheets that are high-contrast, uncluttered and enlarged copies, personal copies of storybooks, additional time to review the material before story time, preferential seating during circle time and other class activities, computer monitors and televisions at eye level (and with fonts enlarged), a slant board for table work, verbal warnings when gradation or lighting conditions are about to change and breaks in tasks that require extended visual attention. Older children may use adaptive technology, like closed-circuit televisions, which would be specified in the IEP.

If your child has difficulty making and maintaining eye contact, you may want to include a goal that addresses that issue, as well as other social skills. If your child is sensitive to bright lights, you may want one set of overhead lights turned off in the classroom or curtains to cover the windows. You may request that your child not have a desk that faces a window and that the teacher remind her to wear a hat and sunglasses every time she goes outside at school.

Implementing the IEP

After you and the school team develop the IEP, you will need to review and sign it. You must grant written permission before the IEP can go into effect. Make sure that you are very comfortable with the language and goals in the IEP, as it grants your permission for the school to provide on-going special education services for your child, and serves as a record of what the school is required to do or provide for your child. Modifications to the IEP can be made at any time, but the entire document is reviewed only once a year. If you believe your child is not learning or making progress, or has achieved the goals sooner than expected, request (in writing) that a meeting be scheduled to revise the IEP.

If you think the school or teacher is not following the IEP, outline your concerns in writing and send them to the school and/or district administrator. E-mail can be very effective because it can be forwarded, a copy will remain in your records and it is very clear when you sent the document.

Finally, it is important to see yourself as part of your child's education team. Make sure your viewpoints are considered, and also work with the service providers to reinforce skills at home. Be sure you understand what you can do to encourage your child's development, and also what accommodations he needs at home to do his homework.

IEPs and Private School

Children who attend private school have limited special education rights under federal law. If you decide to send your child to private school, she is still entitled to an IEP through the public school system, but there is no guarantee that it will be implemented at your particular private school. Each school district is different, and some will provide services in a private school while others will not. Developing an IEP that you will not use in a public school may seem unnecessary, but the evaluation process, as well as the document, can help you understand what accommodations your child will need in a school setting.

If you would like to explore developing an IEP for your child, the first step is to call the local public school and explain that you have a visually impaired child and need to schedule an evaluation for her. She will have to go through the whole evaluation process, which covers all areas of development, not just vision. The school will then schedule a meeting to develop an IEP for her and create specific educational goals based on the vision impairment and any other delays noted during the evaluation.

The IEP meeting ends with the placement decision. This is when you tell the public school that you are "declining placement" and have chosen to send your child to private school. At this point, you should request a Service Plan – a document used in private schools that is similar to an IEP, but without the goals. Some school districts will agree to do this for your child, others will not.

If your school district declines to provide any services, or help you create a Service Plan, you are still legally entitled to a copy of the IEP. It is helpful to have either a Service Plan or a copy of the IEP when meeting with the educators at your private school. A written description and evaluation of your child's educational needs, created by the local school district, can be a persuasive tool in getting the accommodations your child needs in the private school setting.

Section 504 Plan

When a child has a disability that does not adversely impact the child's educational performance, the school may recommend a "Section 504 Plan" instead of an IEP. A 504 Plan is a legal document that outlines services in the school setting for your child. It is much less formal in its creation and implementation than an IEP and requires no comprehensive evaluation. Instead, it relies on consensus to determine a need for services. The plan may cover the same types of accommodations that an IEP would cover, but does not require reevaluation, nor does it guarantee an independent evaluation if the school determines that services are not necessary. Under a 504 Plan, fewer procedural safeguards are available to children with disabilities than under an IEP or an IFSP. Because a 504 Plan has no educational goals, and is only a documentation of necessary accommodations, you should pursue an IEP if your child's low vision has any impact on her academic performance.

Even a child who is not eligible for an IEP may still have needs that should be addressed in a legal manner. For instance, a child might have not have any noticeable difficulty reading small print or regular computer fonts, or navigating her environment , but her parents nonetheless want a written agreement that details the need for accommodations such as lighting modifications or keyboarding instruction. These kinds of accommodations are often worked out informally between school staff and parents, but a 504 Plan makes clear what the school is responsible for doing. This can be particularly helpful when school staff changes, or when your child moves to a new school.

Photo courtesy of Positive Exposure, Rick Guidotti

Chapter 9

Adaptive Technology and Assistive Devices

New technology has changed the way that people who are visually impaired access information and use their vision. Children with albinism now have access to a variety of adaptive devices and technologies that can enhance their vision and help them accomplish everyday tasks. Many low tech adaptations also offer inexpensive solutions that can make a major difference in your child's life. This chapter describes some of the basic devices and accommodations your child may find helpful.

Your state office for the visually impaired may have a lending library where you can borrow different equipment to try out. If your state does not provide the technology you believe your child needs, contact NOAH or your local Lion's Club for more information and assistance.

What is Adaptive Technology?

Adaptive technology is any kind of device or aid that can accommodate, enhance or improve your child's vision. Teaching your child to use adaptive technology can increase his independence and self-esteem by improving his access to information. Simply put, adaptive technology helps to level the playing field for your child. Examples include hand-held magnifiers, glare screens for computer monitors, closed-circuit televisions, and computer software that enlarges images on the screen or converts text into an audio format. Technology improves on a daily basis, so you and your child should be prepared to do further research

on the latest innovations. A simple Internet search of the term "low vision assistive device" should provide you with the latest technological advances. Your vision teacher will also be able to help you learn more about what is available when your child is ready.

Introducing Adaptive Technology

Most professionals agree that you can begin giving your child adaptive technology as early as age three. Early introduction of adaptive devices makes it easier for your child to accept and feel comfortable using this technology. Children as young as three years old can safely play with monoculars and magnifiers. Of course, your child's temperament will dictate how and when you introduce different tools. It is better to wait and have success, than to push and get resistance.

Be prepared to try many products and programs before your child finds the perfect fit. Just as children have different learning styles, one particular piece of equipment may be more suited to your child's particular needs than another. The best way to find out what works is to observe how your child interacts with different equipment and to ask open-ended questions. Encourage your child to try out new devices in a variety of settings and for an extended period of time.

Some children with albinism do not want to use anything to accommodate vision when reading or writing close up. Furthermore, many books used in kindergarten and first grade have large enough type that children often prefer to hold the book close rather than use a magnifier. This is fine, as long as your child knows there is assistance available and can use it if necessary. As your child gets older and the font size in age-appropriate books gets smaller, he may find a greater need for adaptive devices and technology.

Using adaptive devices draws attention to a child's visual impairment, and some children may have difficulty coping with that. As a result, they may be reluctant to use assistive devices. However, children in kindergarten and first grade are open-minded and more receptive to differences, and are likely to respond with curiosity rather than disapproval to the devices and accommodations your child needs to do well in class. Moreover, children at this age often think magnifiers and monoculars are "cool," and are supportive of their use in the classroom.

One way to make the use of these devices more acceptable is to ask your TVI to make a presentation to the class and let the children experiment with a variety of devices, from monoculars to a closed-circuit TV. Also, suggest that the children work with the TVI to devise the rules for use of the adaptive device, and put the rules on a small poster to hang nearby.

Low Tech Assistive Devices

Many easy-to-use products can help to accommodate vision, decrease glare, and alleviate neck strain and eye fatigue for a child with albinism. And many of these can be adapted for home use, or are portable. Thus you can teach your child to take his accommodations with him. This will be an increasingly important skill, as your child learns to read and navigate the world on his own.

Near Vision Aids: Magnifiers and Reading Glasses

Magnifiers and reading glasses are easy and inexpensive devices that can accommodate your child's near vision. A magnifier is a small magnification lens available in different strengths and sizes. It can be hand-held, worn on a lanyard around the neck or rest on a small stand. It is primarily used to help with anything your child would read or see at close range, such as a book or picture. As with all adaptive devices, allow your child to test lots of magnifiers to find the perfect one. Magnifiers are most commonly used for reading small print, which usually isn't an issue for young children. However, if your child has access to a small magnifier, and is comfortable using one, he may be more successful with it when he is older.

Just because a magnifier has strong magnification, does not mean it is easy to use. Big, bulky magnifiers will be too cumbersome for small children, while thin magnifiers may be too weak to be of much help. A TVI, low vision specialist or eye care professional should be part of the process when selecting these devices for your child to ensure the best fit.

Reading glasses will usually not be necessary or helpful until your child reaches first grade. Reading glasses will help to alleviate eye strain

Photo courtesy of Linda Wood

> All kids should find a good, small magnifier that works for them – one they can carry in their pocket. To this day, I feel naked without mine, even around the house. I really didn't start carrying one around until I went to college, but I wish I had sooner. I keep it in my left front jeans pocket and I have no problem pulling it out to use in any situation – menus, voting, the bank, at work or shopping. I don't even think twice about it.
>
> Joni Vella
> Cudahy, WI
> adult with albinism

and fatigue by enabling your child to focus on text more effectively. Your child will still hold the book or paper close to her eyes, but not as close. In addition, reading glasses may reduce your child's need to bend over the desk or book, which will decrease neck tension. Even with reading glasses on, your child will likely still hold material close to his eyes, and will move close to the computer screen. Contrary to popular opinion, this will not damage his eyes. In fact, it is a good example of how your child will seek out accommodations that best suit his own vision.

Distance Vision Aids: Binoculars, Monoculars and Bioptics

Binoculars, monoculars and bioptics are magnifying devices used to

115

enhance distance vision. Not all people with albinism use these devices, but they can be an important tool for your child. Among low vision devices, binoculars are the best ones to introduce first. Allow your child to play with a set of binoculars both inside and outside. Inexpensive binoculars designed for children are widely available. Go to a sporting event where everyone uses binoculars. Take a walk and locate certain large items using the binoculars. Have Daddy make silly faces from across the room and let your child look at them through the binoculars. Allowing your child to use binoculars to watch his favorite television show may be a good way for him to develop skills in a fun way.

Once your child is comfortable with a pair of binoculars, you can let him try a monocular. A monocular is half of a binocular and is only used by one eye at a time. Monoculars may be useful in reading the chalkboard at school or the wall-mounted menu at a restaurant, or in watching a play, a show or a sporting event. Some monoculars can be adjusted for close-up viewing too.

A low vision optometrist, mobility specialist or low vision therapist can help you select a monocular for your child. It is imperative that your child gets the right kind of monocular for it to be useful. Allow your child to play with the monocular before you purchase it, in order to assess fit, comfort and ease of use. Some people with nystagmus have difficulty adjusting to a monocular because of their eye movement, especially since the monocular only involves one eye. Encourage your child to keep trying and do not expect him to use it for an extended period of time.

Bioptic glasses are regular prescription or nonprescription glasses that have a telescope or some type of smaller monocular mounted on one or both lenses. Larger bioptics are mounted on the top of the lenses, while smaller ones can be mounted in the middle. Some bioptics can be adjusted for both near and distance vision, while others only permit one of the two.

Bioptics can be expensive and take training to use efficiently. The advantage of bioptic glasses for school-aged children is that they do not have to hold a monocular up to the eye. A bioptic user looks through the regular glasses most of the time, but can also look through the bioptics to see an item more clearly. With practice, a bioptic user can shift his gaze easily between the bioptics and the glasses lenses.

Contrast Enhancement Aids

For people with albinism, bigger isn't always better. Increasing the contrast of text is often more effective than increasing the size of text. Black felt-tipped pens and dark-lined paper can make writing easier for some children with low vision. In addition, number three pencils (as opposed to traditional number two pencils) and bright-colored chalk can also help students with albinism. Writing guides – templates with open areas to write in – can help people with albinism write in straight lines or complete precision tasks such as writing checks. Colored filters can make it easier to see certain colors. For example, a yellow filter can make light blue letters appear darker and easier to read.

Overlays, Contact Paper and Cloth

A few simple solutions can help children who are sensitive to glare and have difficulty discerning objects in poor contrast. A sheet of dark-colored contact paper applied to a surface improves the contrast of objects placed on top, making it easier to see toys, food or other objects. A baby playing on the floor gets the same benefit from lying on a dark cloth. To reduce glare from the pages of a book, place a colored overlay, such as a pastel yellow overhead projector sheet, on top of any page with a bright background. Make sure the contact paper or overlay has a matte finish because a shiny or glossy finish will only make the glare worse.

Elevating, Angling and Raising Objects

Bringing books, toys and other objects closer to your child's eyes will decrease his tendency to lean over to see them. When your child is playing on a flat surface, consider the height of the surface, and watch to see whether he is leaning over to see what he is doing. One way to let your child get close to what he's doing without having to bend over is to use a vertical art easel. Many of them come with a magnetized surface and a chalkboard. Putting paper up on the easel is a great way for your child to practice coloring, painting and writing because he can get as close as he needs to without bending over.

When your child is learning how to write and form letters, consider using a slant board or platform to alleviate eye, neck and back strain. A "slant board" is a commercially available elevated writing surface, and works like an old-fashioned school desk. Slant boards are often provided by a TVI, or through your school or state organization. You can also look in specialty catalogs, such as that of the American Printing House for the Blind (available online at **www.aph.org**). Lap desks and book stands can also help.

> " A typical slant board may be bigger than your child, making it impractical to use. Our son could barely lift his in kindergarten! Instead, we took a large three-ring binder, and attached a heavy clip to it. We let our child decorate the cover with his artwork and class pictures, and we used it to save and store special art and completed work. He was proud of how it turned out, and less reluctant to use it. This was a good substitute, and was very portable. "
>
> Susan Leslie DuBois
> Arlington, VA
> parent of two children with albinism

High Tech Assistive Devices

Computers are now a part of every child's life. Many children are exposed to simple computer games from the age of two or three, either at home or at pre-school. Between the games and the educational software, computers offer many positive activities for your child. A computer is also a very easy tool to modify for your child's low vision. The following adaptations are easy and will go a long way towards making computer use less challenging and more fun for your child. Consider requesting these changes at your child's pre-school or elementary school. Some of these accommodations, like glare control, font size and mouse pointer size, can be included in your child's IEP.

Your child probably positions himself to be within seven to ten inches from the computer monitor. While this can cause eye strain, fatigue and poor posture, it will not damage his eyes. However, by making the computer station more ergonomically suited to your child, you will help him use an important tool more effectively and also make the experience more fun.

One easy accommodation is to buy a new computer monitor, after the following considerations:

- Think about a large monitor, such as one with a 21-inch screen.
- Let your child help pick out the monitor. Even minor differences are major to a child who is visually impaired. Evaluate both flat-panel and standard monitors.
- Allow your child to change the settings on the monitor to decrease brightness and increase contrast.
- Check the owner's manual to learn how to set the optimal refresh rate. The more often the screen refreshes, the easier it is on the eyes.

You can also adapt the computer for ease of use by changing certain settings:

- Look at your operating system's accessibility features (in Windows or Macintosh). You may find a magnification program is already installed on your computer.
- Some computer operating systems come with a "high contrast mode." This may be a black screen with white fonts and other bright colors for icons and menus. Your child may find the text easier to see this way.
- You can manually change colors and enlarge the font on your computer's desktop and in the programs. Consider making the desktop a dark color and the screen in the word processing program black with white font. This will decrease the sharp glare of a white screen on the computer. Let your child choose from among all the available fonts.
- Make the mouse pointer bigger, and the tracking speed slower. This is one of the easiest and most effective ways to modify your computer for your child.
- If other computer users in the home do not like the larger fonts and different colors, let each family member create his or her own user login with customized settings for the desktop and other programs. That way, when a user logs into the computer, his or her personal settings will appear.

You will also make computer use easier for your child if you encourage him to learn to touch-type, without looking at the keys, as early as possible. Otherwise your child will have to look at the keys very closely to type, which causes neck strain and fatigue and leads to bad typing habits that are hard to reverse later. Touch-typing is a skill that will serve him well when he is older and has to write papers and do homework.

Finally, consider the keyboard and how to maximize its usefulness for your child. Try teaching your child to use keyboard commands rather than the mouse, because using the mouse can be difficult for children with visual impairments. For example, teach your child to save a document by pressing the "Control" and "S" keys together rather than by moving the mouse to and clicking on the small "Save" icon in the toolbar. Check the help section on your computer to learn the many keyboard commands. You may also want to explore purchasing a large-button keyboard, available online from an adaptive technology retailer. The large buttons with high-contrast lettering reduce the need to bend over the keyboard to distinguish the different letters.

Adaptive Technology Software Programs

A wide variety of software is available to assist computer users who have low vision. From simple magnification software to voice-capable reading software, there are many different options. ZoomText and MAGic are two computer screen magnification programs designed specifically for people with low vision. These programs offer different levels of magnification, can change contrast quickly, change the mouse pointer's size and color, offer speech output options and have more features your child may find helpful. You can download free trial versions of these programs from the manufacturer's websites. Please see the Resources section for more information.

Macintosh has built-in software for people with low vision. VoiceOver is available on most Macintosh operating systems and features screen enlargement and reading capabilities. In addition, audio books are widely available in a variety of formats. Most popular children's stories are available through your public library. You can also register with a special service listed in the Resource section that provides audio material for children with low vision. Acquaint your child with audio books so they can be an option when eye fatigue is an issue. Audio books are also a great option for car trips.

Photo courtesy of Positive Exposure, Rick Guidotti

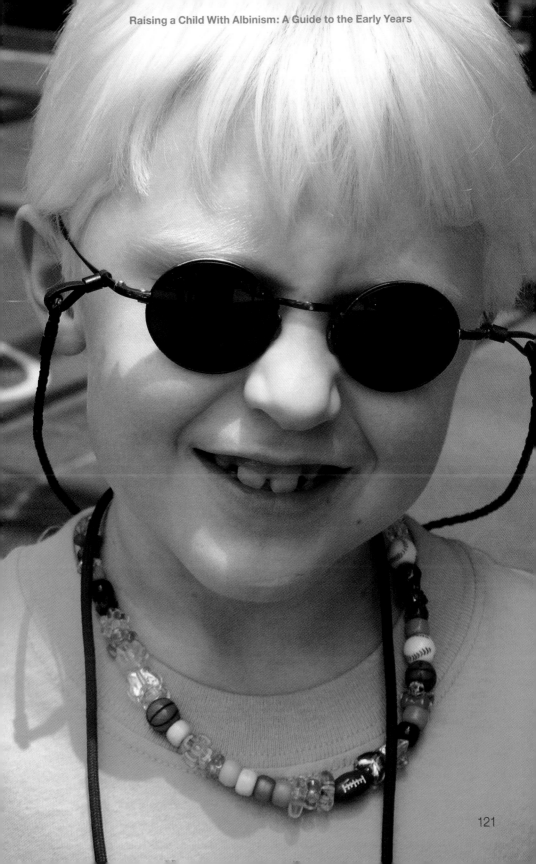

Closed-Circuit Television

A Closed-circuit television (CCTV) is a video magnifier that uses a camera to project a magnified image onto a monitor or television screen. Many students use them in classrooms to help with the fine print in textbooks and to read charts and maps. CCTV systems also allow the user to adjust the size, brightness, and contrast of the magnified image to best match the user's vision. The user can even read white letters on a black background to decrease glare. CCTV systems have historically been far more expensive and far less portable than other near-vision aids. However, new CCTVs are smaller, more versatile, more portable, and less expensive than their predecessors.

To use one of these devices, the child places the book or piece of paper on the platform of the video magnifier and the camera projects the image onto the screen. Many video magnifiers accommodate writing under the camera so your child can fill in a worksheet. This device is very helpful for children with albinism because they can change colors and contrast easily. They can turn a bright white page black or dark blue and convert the font to be white or yellow. Moreover, looking at the text on the vertical screen rather than on the horizontal desk or table allows the child to hold his head straight and avoid neck and back strain.

Some video magnifiers have a distance-viewing mode that allows a student in a classroom to focus the camera on the chalkboard, overhead projector image or classroom monitor and magnify it on the screen at the child's desk. Smaller, more portable video magnifiers are also available. The print size in books for children in the early grades should be large enough that a CCTV is unnecessary, but having the use of one by first or second grade can mean that your child is comfortable and adept at using one when the need arises.

Hundreds of other technologies exist for people who are blind or visually impaired. Moreover, educational software can help your child access learning opportunities on the computer. By first grade, you should be thinking about what types of devices would be most helpful for your child. Request an adaptive technology evaluation as part of your child's early intervention or educational services.

Teaching Your Child Responsibility

Teach your child how to clean and care for his low vision aids as soon as you think he is able to do so. Many devices are expensive and provide

One recent technological advance embraced by people with albinism is the GPS, or Global Positioning System. GPS is a satellite-based navigation system made up of a network of twenty-four satellites that can provide a user with almost limitless information, including maps, precise directions and the exact location of various commercial establishments. Hand-held GPS units can really help with personal mobility, and those with a voice output that are installed in cars can help low vision drivers find destinations. They are a good example of how quickly technology changes and how it can be adapted for low vision use.

enormous assistance to your child, so help him understand the importance of using and caring for them responsibly. Keep a special bag with his low vision devices ready to grab whenever he needs them.

Photo courtesy of Linda Wood

Chapter 10

The Social Aspects of Albinism

All parents want their children to grow up feeling secure and having a healthy sense of self-esteem. Albinism will have an impact on your child's social development in several key ways. Looking different often affects a child's social acceptance by her peers and her own development of self-esteem. In addition, low vision often contributes to difficulties in developing appropriate social behavior. These factors can make it more challenging to find friends and to develop a healthy attitude about oneself.

This chapter addresses the impact of albinism on social development, and offers strategies for handling the difficulties that may arise. Children with visual impairments often need some extra help in developing certain social skills. At the same time, you may be wondering about how best to discuss albinism with your child and how to manage family dynamics. Helping your child learn how to develop friendships at an early age is very important. The social stigma associated with albinism is an unfortunate part of adolescence for some children, but if they have strong social skills, healthy self-esteem and an ability to make friends, they will overcome this hurdle.

Building Self-Esteem

Self-esteem can be an important shield against the difficulties of life. Self-esteem refers to the way we feel about ourselves: the collection of attitudes and perceptions about our abilities and qualities. **Children with a positive self-esteem have an easier time handling conflicts and are generally optimistic. Children with low self-esteem have a more difficult time meeting challenges and finding solutions to problems.**

Children with albinism may develop low self-esteem for several reasons. They will realize at an early age that they look different from their peers, that they sometimes struggle more with playground activities or with some sports and that their vision is different from that of their friends. It is critical that parents take an active role in helping their child feel good about herself.

Find a great photograph of your family, and put it in a special frame near your child's bed. It will serve as a prominent, visual reminder of her family and her role in it.

Self-esteem, which is caught, not taught, can be defined as feeling capable plus feeling loved. It develops through consistent nurturing and successful achievement of new skills. One way to help your child develop self-esteem is to give her tasks that challenge her abilities, but are within reach. Give your child the opportunity to be successful, after making an effort. Always be sure to praise the effort, not the outcome when she is coloring or building a block tower, so the praise is tied to the ability to perform the task, not to the final product, like how high the tower is, or how neatly the picture is drawn.

Parents have a huge influence on their child's self-esteem and there are many things you can do to help your child develop a positive outlook and high self-regard. The following strategies can help you to create an environment where self-esteem will flourish:

- Practice unconditional love, and give lots of hugs.
- Help your child find a hobby or activity she is good at, and encourage her participation.
- Talk openly and honestly about albinism. This gives your child the message that you accept it. Encourage her to ask you any questions she may have about albinism.
- Discuss any potential differences or limitations in a neutral way.

Photo courtesy of Positive Exposure, Rick Guidotti

For instance, say, "You have to wear glasses (or sit up front during circle time) to help you see better," rather than, "You can't see well, so you have to wear glasses."

- Introduce your child to another child with albinism. If you do not know of anyone with albinism in your area, try finding a pen pal with whom your child can talk on the phone, e-mail, and exchange pictures and stories. This may help your child to feel less isolated.

- Celebrate your child's strengths. You may feel redundant, but praise, praise, praise, your child! Be honest, and don't overdo it, as even pre-schoolers can detect insincerity.

- Discuss the following concept with your child: We all are different, that is what makes us the same! Children with albinism may feel like they are the only students with differences. Explain that all children are different and each is special in a different way.

- Listen carefully. Empathize with your child's concerns and respect her feelings. Redirect negative self-talk.

- Show support. Your child's fears may be calmed just by your acknowledgment of her feelings.

Look for the storybook "All Children Have Different Eyes", which has a child with albinism on the cover and features activities to help children with visual impairments make friends, answer questions about their condition, and handle social challenges. See the website at **www.lowvisionkids.com** or the Resource Section for more information.

Self-esteem can also flourish when a child feels successful at something that has meaning in her world. Help your child find an activity or a hobby that she is good at, so that she can be proud of herself. Competence breeds confidence, and the ability to perform well in your peer group is an important part of developing self-esteem.

I remember going out and buying a pair of rollerblades when the sport was starting to take off in the early 90's. The first time I went rollerblading I was absolutely terrible. I think I fell down about 30 times. However, I stuck with it and practiced every day. Eventually I reached a point where I was able to jump over all sorts of obstacles and was arguably the best rollerblader in my hometown. Of course, by this time the rollerblading craze had come and gone but it was still something that I was known for by my peers and something for which I was respected.

John Schmit
Minneapolis, MN
adult with albinism

Developing Good Social Skills

Children with albinism often struggle to develop appropriate social skills. Many of the key social habits we practice as adults are learned through observation of those around us. For the child with a visual impairment, this is more difficult. One of the more challenging aspects of raising a child with albinism is teaching her these fundamental skills that others learn through casual observation.

As parents, one of our primary roles is to teach children appropriate social behaviors based on the norms of our society and our culture. Three key social skills that are often problematic for children with visual impairments are:

- Making and maintaining good eye contact
- Respecting personal space
- Observing facial expressions and perceiving body language

For example, in cultures where eye contact is important, parents must remember that a child with nystagmus may not recognize the need to look at another person's eyes when speaking. In fact, the act of looking at another person's eyes may make it more difficult for the child to clearly see the person she is talking to, because she is forcing her eyes to focus on a small subset of the person's face. Because children with albinism often do not benefit from maintaining good eye contact in a conversation, they can seem inattentive and uninterested. They must be taught to face the speaker, and gently reminded to make eye contact when necessary.

An effective technique is to gently take your child's face in your hands and physically move her head so her eyes are pointed towards your eyes, and say, "Give me your eyes, please." After a while, the phrase "eyes please" will be enough to cue your youngster to look at you while you are speaking. Teachers and caregivers should be instructed to reinforce this when necessary and it should be made part of an IEP when needed.

A child with a visual impairment also needs to learn to maintain appropriate personal space. A child with albinism may move very close to another person to see that person more easily. However, that closeness makes most people uncomfortable. Offer your child a quick reminder to maintain an appropriate distance and explain that other people may not like having someone stand so close to them. Toddlers have no real problem with this issue, but by four years of age, children begin to develop "comfort zones." You can remind your child to "lean back" or to "give space to your buddies."

Noticing and understanding facial expressions can be challenging for a child with a visual impairment, especially when she is doing her best to respect someone else's personal space. A fun way to work on this is to play "What face am I making?" at the dinner table. Use exaggerated expressions to mimic happy, sad, scared, tired, mad, and have your child guess the expression. The distance created by the table is helpful in training your child to observe from a short distance, and the game is fun too! You can reinforce this concept when reading books with your child, as many stories have great illustrations of emotions. Explain to an older child the non-verbal body language such as arm-crossing and shrugging that are illustrated in the pictures.

Discussing Albinism with Your Child

One of the most important ways to help your child develop a healthy attitude about albinism is to discuss it in an open, honest and neutral way. This means that as a parent, you must be accepting and comfortable

with the condition. It is important for your child to know that you fully accept albinism, and that siblings and other family members understand and accept it too.

The way you choose to discuss albinism with your child is a very personal decision. Some families openly discuss albinism from the very beginning, while others wait until their children are entering school to explain the issue, and some choose to combine the two approaches. You will develop a method that works for your family, but here are some things to consider:

- Your child has been hearing the word "albinism" since she was diagnosed. She has also heard countless comments about her white hair and her eyes. An open discussion with your child can help promote acceptance on her part. She may be confused if you do not discuss albinism with her, as she has doubtlessly heard you discuss it with others, either by answering questions about her appearance or by telling a family member about a recent doctor's appointment.

- If you wait until your child is five or six to have "The Talk," her condition might come across as a problem. Children are remarkably astute, and can sense if you are uncomfortable about discussing the topic.

- Your discussion should be age-appropriate and need not be too specific. No little child can grasp the intricacies of genetics, but a simple discussion of "you get a little bit from Mommy and a little bit from Daddy" should do for a curious four-year-old.

At some point, every parent will face questions from his or her child about why she looks different, or why she can't see very well. Again, answering honestly is best, but you don't have to give too much information, either. The goal is to help your child define her albinism, not let albinism define your child.

Some people struggle with how to discuss their child's visual impairment, particularly with respect to the possibility of driving some day. There is no reason to tell a young child that she will never drive. You cannot know that yet because it is impossible to predict what advancements will be made in adaptive technology in the coming years. Moreover, the information is not pertinent to a six-year-old. There are countless stories within the NOAH community of young people who were told they would never drive – and then did. A realistic, honest answer is the best approach. For example: "I don't know if you will drive when you grow up. You might be able to use special glasses that will help you, or you might choose to live in a city where don't need a car to get around." As your child gets older and more mature, you will have ample opportunity to discuss the impact of her vision on the things she'd like to do.

> " I never take driving for granted because I grew up being told I would never be able to drive. Driving while being legally blind has a lot of funny moments associated with it. I pull into a handicapped spot and get out of my car and someone actually asks, "Why are you using that spot? Are you blind or something?" When I say, "Yes, and I park here because of poor depth perception and so I can find my car," the look on their face is priceless! "
>
> Beth Wiggs
> Arlington, TX
> adult with albinism

You can discuss albinism with your child in many different ways, and what matters most is choosing one with which you are comfortable. Only you know what your child is ready to understand and appreciate, and what age is best to begin the discussion. Here are some simple strategies for you to adapt to your own circumstances:

- When strangers ask questions or make comments, use them as an opportunity to offer a simple explanation and praise your child's appearance. "Yes, isn't her hair amazing? It's white because she has albinism."
- When the NOAH newsletter arrives, share it with your child, and chat about the pictures of people with albinism.
- If you are fortunate enough to have an albinism playgroup in your area, use the group's get-togethers to discuss albinism with your child. They can also be a great way to get ideas from other parents.

> My son has OCA, and he has known it since he was a very small child. We always spoke openly about it, and never felt that it caused him to be teased or bullied (simply because he knew the name of his condition). He has always been very proud of who he is and equally comfortable with telling other children why he is pale and his eyes move. I think having a name for something somehow makes it less threatening and makes children less fearful, and I feel that being open and honest allows him to come to terms with his differences and accept himself for who he is.
>
> Jeannine Stearns
> Boxborough, MA
> parent of a child with albinism

One way to help your school-age child understand albinism is to create a "social story" together. A social story is a scrapbook that presents a kid-friendly portrait of your child in age-appropriate language. It should include pictures and drawings, and should focus on your child's whole life – not just her albinism. Your child's story should be tailored to her personality, and should address issues that concern her. The tone, depth and length will vary according to each child, but here is a sample outline of what your child's social story can contain:

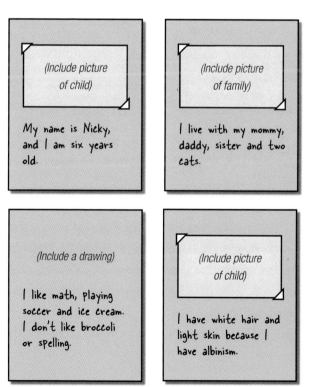

(Include picture of child)

My name is Nicky, and I am six years old.

(Include picture of family)

I live with my mommy, daddy, sister and two cats.

(Include a drawing)

I like math, playing soccer and ice cream. I don't like broccoli or spelling.

(Include picture of child)

I have white hair and light skin because I have albinism.

People with albinism do not have the usual amounts of a pigment — or color — in their skin, hair or eyes.

Most kids with albinism have white hair and blue eyes, even though many of their parents have darker hair and eyes. There are people with albinism all over the world, and more than 18,000 here in America!

Having albinism means I have to be extra careful to protect my skin and eyes when I am out in the sun. My mom got me special sunscreen that smells like coconuts. I love it! I also wear a hat and dark sunglasses when it's sunny.

(Include picture of soccer game)

I play on a soccer team, and once I scored a goal!

I wear glasses to help me see better. So do my sister, my mother and my father. Some of my friends do, too! Sometimes it is hard for me to see things that are far away, and this makes me mad. I can always ask for help!

(Include picture of kids playing)

I have lots of friends with albinism. I have other friends who have different abilities, too. We do fun things together!

Some kids like to share their stories at school, and some prefer to keep them private. The process of creating the social story is almost as important as how you use it. Talking with your child and deciding what to put on the pages can give you invaluable insight into how your child feels about her condition. Creating a social story can also be a great way for your child to develop a strategy for talking about her albinism.

> I was born in 1980, before NOAH was even founded. There wasn't much information available about albinism, and I didn't understand my condition. Kids today should be taught about albinism from an early age so that they can educate their peers and teachers, and advocate for themselves. This should help stop bullying before it even starts – it all goes back to educating people!
>
> Jessica Trask
> Watervliet, NY
> adult with albinism

Don't be alarmed if your child expresses strong negative feelings about her albinism, or says she hates her white hair. It is important to recognize that these negative feelings are a normal part of growing up. You should refrain from correcting your child. Instead, acknowledge her feelings, let her know it is OK to feel that way, and that you will always listen. You can say something like "I understand. Sometimes it's tough when people always notice something about you and ask questions. You can always tell me when something like this bothers you. Maybe we can work together to help you figure out what to say." You can follow up by asking her to identify something she likes about herself.

Making Friends

Making friends is one of the key social activities that children begin to learn at an early age. The suggestions below are a sampling of ideas that have worked for other parents of children with albinism. Depending on your child's temperament and personality, some of these suggestions may be more effective than others. As a parent, your job is to try different strategies and find the ones that work for your child so she eventually learns how to make friends. Having friends can make the social issues associated with albinism much easier. The following suggestions should help you encourage your child to build friendships.

The Pre-school Years

- Take your child to playgroups with other children the same age. Watch how she behaves and guide the interactions when necessary. Remind your child to ask to "see it up close for just a minute," and explain (when necessary) that your child just needs to hold the book or toy up close to see it better. Children from three years and up usually accept this explanation without question.

- Talk openly with other parents about your child's albinism and educate them about the actual impact of the vision impairment. Dispel any myths or concerns that they have about their child playing with your child. Most people don't have experience with low vision so don't be offended, just let them know how it impacts your child.

- Remind caregivers that your child may not see the visual cues given by other children. Ask for their active participation in helping your child notice these cues. Normally-sighted children often don't need the same assistance, so you are asking for something that might not be the norm.

- Ensure that your child's IEP has a specific goal for making friends – this will keep it foremost in the caregiver's mind.

- Begin to explore your child's interests. Enroll her in music, movement, gymnastics or other activities. Do not assume she cannot do a certain activity. Encourage her to try it.

- Consider hosting neighborhood playgroups, and having birthday parties with lots of fun activities.

- Invite other children to your house – one at a time – and try to foster reciprocity. However, if the other parents don't invite your child to play, just keep inviting theirs. This is not the time to make sure it all comes out even.

The Early School Days: Kindergarten through Second Grade:
- Continue the above activities.
- Ask your child which classmates or playmates she likes and invite them over, one at a time, to help develop the friendships outside of school.
- If possible, volunteer in your child's classroom, so you can have a good perspective on how she is doing in school.
- Ask about your child's classmates: Who are their friends? How are they doing? Ask open-ended questions about what these classmates do with the other children at school.

- Create, refine or enhance IEP goals so that friendships are a continued focus.

- Help your child become more involved in activities outside the home. Sign her up for scouts, sports, music or other programs.

- Host fun birthday parties and invite kids in the neighborhood, the school or other groups in which your child participates. Even if your child is not invited to many other children's parties, keep inviting them to yours.

- Within reason, try to ensure that your child has the latest toys and games, or at least understands what they are and how to play them. You will need to teach your child how to play most games, as she can not pick them up just by watching the other children. The objective is to help your child be socially literate and able to play with her peers. Practicing these skills ahead of time can reduce your child's frustration.

Looking Ahead

It is important to continue to discuss albinism with your child so that she may answer questions and respond when other children begin to notice and comment. **When something bad happens with a peer, talk about it with your child. Understand first how your child perceives the episode, and then discuss what she could do differently next time.**

Talk about feelings with your child and be a problem-solver. Listen – don't judge. Remember that you cannot know first-hand how your child is feeling, or what happened at school, so you need to listen to her description of these things. Keep in mind that her interpretation of the situation may not be the reality – it is what she thinks happened. You may need to get further information from teachers, other parents, or other children to adequately assess the situation.

When observing your child at play, watch how she interacts with the other children. Be mindful of the visual cues that your child may be missing during playtime. Ask your child's teachers or other caregivers about how she is doing socially. Is your child included in activities on the playground or during school? Ask your child what games she played

on the playground during the day, or whom she sat with at lunch that day. Is your child unintentionally doing things to alienate other children? Exploring these questions will provide you with important insights into what social skills she may be lacking.

Talk to your child privately about how she interacts with other children, and discuss your observations. For example, if your child regularly stays on the sidelines at recess, talk to her at home about why she is not playing with the other children. Help her identify how to handle the situation differently by asking open-ended questions. Then, work with your child to come up with solutions. Suggesting games that do not rely on distance vision can help, too.

For older children, explain that a playmate may misinterpret your child's behavior. For example, if your child cannot recognize a friend from a distance, and that friend says "hello" from across the playground, the friend may interpret your child's failure to respond as a rejection. You will learn that everyone recognizes your child, and there is no easy way for her to distinguish other children across the playground yelling "hello" to her. Teaching your child to respond with a smile and wave to everyone who says "hello" is a good strategy. This allows her to acknowledge a friendly greeting and perhaps to move closer or ask someone else who it was that said "hello." Over time, your child may learn to recognize the sound of a friend's voice, or determine who is speaking based on the clothing that person is wearing. Smiling and waving are a good first step in portraying friendly behavior towards other children.

Story time and "show and tell" activities can also be challenging for a child with visual impairments. Your child may need to see the book or item up close and become frustrated if she can't. Other children may be reluctant to give up their book or item because sharing is a tough concept for all kids. Teach your child to explain that she needs to see it up close 'for just a minute,' and have her give the item right back. Not only does this help prevent fights, it teaches sharing and important self-advocacy skills.

The "A" Word

It is unlikely that a person will approach you in the grocery store and ask, "Does your child have albinism?" Most often, parents are asked if their child is an albino. **For many people, the word "albino" is considered a slur, and evokes feelings of anger and prejudice. However, while some people do use this term as an insult, most are just unfamiliar with the more acceptable phrase "person with albinism."**

Use of these terms has been widely discussed in the NOAH community for years, and opinions vary about which is preferable. The term "person with albinism" emerged after the Americans with Disabilities Act passed in 1990 and the country began to move toward person-centered terms. "People with disabilities" replaced "the disabled." The rationale behind this person-centered language is to put the individual ahead of the condition. When you refer to someone as "an epileptic" or "a paraplegic," you are essentially defining the whole person by his or her condition. The word albino reduces a person to one characteristic, whereas the term "person with albinism" identifies the condition as an aspect of the individual. Even though the distinction (and the phrase "person with albinism") seems a bit long and unwieldy, it is very important to many in the community to be recognized in this way.

While most people prefer the term "person with albinism," your child will certainly be called an albino – mostly out of benign ignorance, but occasionally as an insult. As parents, we must frame the issue so our children feel no shame when they hear the word albino. Most people who use the word albino are not trying to be rude or disrespectful, they simply don't realize that the word can be hurtful to people with albinism. Pay particular attention to the situation in which the word is used. The context, setting, demeanor, and intonation of the people who use the term to label or describe your child will tell a lot about their motives and whether they are misinformed or rude.

As in many other situations related to albinism, the way you react to someone calling your child albino sets the tone for your child's reaction too. Very young children are not going to understand what the word albino means, or that it can carry negative connotations. Your child will take her cues from you on how to respond when she hears the word used to describe her. If you appear to get agitated and upset, she will learn to get agitated and upset. If, however, you politely explain to the individual using the term that it is sometimes used derogatorily and so the preferable term is "person with albinism," your child will also learn to use that tactic to address the issue.

> When I was five, I was "an albino." When I was 15, I was "a person with albinism." Now, I think I'm somewhere in between. It was around the age of 18 that I realized that the condition of albinism was mine to own. I once asked a long-time NOAH friend if he was offended when people called him an albino. He shrugged and said, "No. It's what I am." I started to realize that these words – or rather the one word in particular – that I allowed to hurt me for so many years was actually pretty accurate. And, more importantly, it was just a word.
>
> Just because I've come to terms with the word "albino" doesn't mean that I prefer it. I use it with my friends and often try to slip it in once or twice when I'm first explaining the condition of albinism to someone, just to reiterate that I won't jump you if use the more common word. (As many of us have seen, the world at large is much more familiar with the word "albino" than the word "albinism," like it or not.) I've found that sometimes it helps to use words that people are more familiar with.
>
> Of course, in a situation like this, where someone is being introduced to the topic of albinism, I always make sure to include the caveat that, although I'm OK with it, some people with albinism do find the word "albino" offensive, and that not everybody will just laugh and shrug it off if you call them that.
>
> Kelsey Thompson
> Chicago, IL
> adult with albinism

Sometimes you may choose to ignore the term albino, or may even use it yourself when explaining albinism to others. If your child hears you use the term casually, she will attach no stigma to it, and will view its use by others as simple ignorance that can be ignored or corrected, as she sees fit. Your reaction will help your child shape hers.

Albinism and Siblings

When one child in the family has a genetic disorder, it is only natural to consider what the impact will be on other children, and whether any future children inherit the same disorder. It is no different in the albinism community. Few families have a subsequent pregnancy without considering the possibility of having another child with albinism.

While the decision to have other children is deeply personal, there are some things to consider about having another child with albinism. There is absolutely nothing you can do to pre-select genetic traits, and absent fairly invasive genetic testing, there is no way to predict the presence of albinism. While every parent wants the healthiest child possible, there are some positive aspects to having a second child with albinism.

First, the diagnosis won't come as a surprise. You already know exactly what you need to do, and how to do it. You've had experience with sunscreen, ophthalmologists and early intervention services. You understand that your child has limitless potential, and that she will continue to thrive and develop.

Second, you don't have to worry about inadvertently treating your children differently. You have a level playing field, and you will avoid fights about why one child has to wear a hat and sunglasses outdoors, or gets to sit right in front of the television.

> We have two children with OCA1a, and the learning curve with our son Nick was pretty steep. By the time our daughter Katy came around, we were seasoned pros, and worried more about whether she'd eat and sleep as well as her brother than if she'd have pigment.
>
> Having two children with albinism is challenging, but I love knowing that they'll always be there for each other.
>
> Susan Leslie DuBois
> Arlington, VA
> parent of children with albinism

Third, and perhaps most importantly, you have a built-in peer group for your children. They will never know what it is like to have albinism and be alone. There will always be someone in their life who can relate to them in a way that we, as parents without albinism, cannot. Your children might not always get along, but they will always be allies.

In a family with multiple siblings with and without albinism, the typically-pigmented children will learn first-hand about differences, and will develop tolerance and empathy. Enlist their assistance in caring for a younger sibling with albinism by asking them to help keep track of glasses and hats. This will help them understand the importance of sun protection, but will also make them feel special.

Older siblings with albinism may have difficulty when their younger siblings master visual tasks with greater ease. Your child with albinism may display anger or jealousy, which are both normal responses. Try to listen with empathy, and discuss the issue neutrally. Talk about how all people have strengths and weaknesses, and look for an example in your own family to illustrate the point. A good strategy is to always be open to discuss the issue, and look for talents in your child that you can nurture. Don't let albinism become an issue between your children, and try as much as possible to have the same expectations and to provide the same experiences for all of your children.

Creating a Community

Establishing personal relationships with other people and families in the albinism community is one of the most important things you can do for your child, as well as for yourself. It is beneficial for your child to have early experiences with other children with albinism, because she will feel

Since my third child was diagnosed with albinism, I've worried that I've spent too much time focused on her needs at the expense of my two older children, and have wondered how having a child with albinism affects their lives. I've realized that my older children will have a relationship with their sister Lyra long after I'm gone, and I want it to be a positive relationship. I want them all to be close, and to love and care for each other. I try to remember that as I raise my children, I am laying the foundation for their evolving relationship as siblings.

My older daughter Rebekah wants to know everything she can about albinism and how it will affect Lyra. She wants to learn Braille and about the anatomy of eye. If we can't answer her questions, she'll look it up. I'm proud that she's is protective of Lyra and wants to be able to answer other people's questions.

My son Dominick is more laid back and until recently he hasn't really asked questions related to Lyra's albinism. When she was born, we talked to him about it, but not in great detail. He was four, so he didn't really understand what it all meant. However, when Dominick noticed Lyra's nystagmus for the first time, he was truly impressed by the "trick" that she could do with her eyes and wished he could do it. I tried to explain it to him, but he was convinced it was her cool trick and he was going to learn how to do it too.

Mashawna Thompson
Edwardsville, KS
parent of a child with albinism

less isolated as she grows up if she has other friends who look like her, and share her experience. It also helps many parents feel less isolated to have their own peer group of other parents who know what they're going through. Building relationships with other families is also a great way to share information and resources.

There are many ways to meet other families with children who have albinism. Your Early Intervention Services provider, pediatrician, pediatric ophthalmologist, optometrist, TVI or occupational therapist might know other children with albinism, but privacy issues may restrict what kind of information they can share with other families. To meet other families in your area, prepare a letter granting permission to give your contact information to others and ask your care providers to share it with people they think you might like to meet.

The Albinism Online Community (AOC) on NOAH's website is an excellent place to meet other families, and to look for groups in your area.

> "The Washington, D.C., NOAH play-group now has more than twenty families from Washington, Maryland and Virginia, but started with a post on the NOAH web board by Kelly Hoynoski, the mother of a young son with albinism offering to host a gathering for area families. Several families responded, and we were soon meeting monthly to share stories and to provide the kids with a group of peers and friends.
>
> We share information about pediatric ophthalmologists, school issues, sunglasses and sports, and many other tips and tools that we each use to help our children maximize their potential. But the most important thing that we have shared over the years is our feelings. Many of us came to the playgroup a bit shell-shocked from a new diagnosis, or still struggling to accept albinism. It has been enormously comforting to talk to people who have had the same experience. Many times we've had extended families, particularly grandparents, join our gatherings. I think it has helped our families better understand and accept albinism by being exposed to our playgroup.
>
> As much as we think we've been helped as parents by participating in this group, we know that it is our children who will benefit the most from these special friendships. We don't expect them to all be best friends, but we believe that they will be better off always knowing other kids who are just like themselves."
>
> Susan Leslie DuBois
> Arlington, VA
> parent of children with albinism

Try posting a message asking if there are other families who live near yours. You can correspond by e-mail at first, and you may begin to plan regular get-togethers.

Another way to begin creating a community is to attend a NOAH bi-annual conference, a regional mini-conference or any of the other activities sponsored by NOAH. Attending a NOAH event is the best way to meet and see lots of other people with albinism and other parents. It's also a great way to get up-to-date information, ideas and empathy from experts and experienced parents. Children and families make lasting friendships through these conferences and keep in touch through e-mail and by attending other NOAH events.

A community can consist of an online chat group, a regular play-group in your area, or quarterly get-togethers in a nearby city. The idea is to give your child an independent reference point for all that she is (or soon will be) experiencing. As she grows older, a peer group with the same experiences will be invaluable.

Teasing and Bullying

Many parents fear their child will be teased because of her albinism. The good news is that society no longer tolerates the kind of bullying that you may remember as a child. However, teasing is a fact of life for almost all children, and repeated teasing or social isolation can having a lasting impact on your child's life.

As children develop, they all start to realize that there are differences among kids. At first, when they are younger, differences are interesting for them. They are very curious about why and how someone is different. In general, they are accepting of differences, unless adults around them socialize them to be afraid of those who are different.

At around nine or ten years old, those differences become a way for them to create little groups that sometimes exclude other children. That is the age at which bullying may increase, often driven by kids trying to define themselves and their peer group. Bullies tend to pick on and exploit major differences – in the child who is overweight or underweight, wears glasses or has a disability or a physical difference.

Bullying occurs when a person or a group repeatedly seeks to hurt someone who is weaker. Bullying can be active, when it involves physical contact like hitting or tripping, or can consist of verbal teasing or name-calling. It can also be passive, when it involves social rejection or exclusion from activities. Bullying is a painful problem for many children, and studies show that almost half of all children experience it at one point in their lives. Nonetheless, children with albinism are an easy target for bullies, as they often look very different from other children.

It is important to distinguish bullying from peer conflict, which is normal at all ages and grade levels. Peer conflict includes aggression and hurtful remarks, but is very different from bullying in that it does not include an imbalance of power. Bullying has three main features:

- It is a repeated negative action targeted at an individual.
- It involves an imbalance of power. The victim of bullying often lacks the skills to cope with the negative attention, and has trouble defending herself.
- Bullying is characterized by an unequal effect. The bully often shows no emotion, and feels justified in his action, while the victim may withdraw, cry or act out in anger.

The scope of this book is limited to the age when bullying isn't really a problem, but there are some anti-bullying strategies and suggestions you can use if you suspect your child is being bullied.

- Help your child develop strong friendships. This may be the single most important thing you can do to help protect your child.
- Talk openly about bullying and what it can mean. Explain to your child that the bully's true goal is to get a response.
- Maintain a dialogue with your child on a daily basis, and ask open-ended questions about her day.
- Involve your child in the solution. Ask what she thinks should be done. How did she respond? What worked and what didn't?
- Help your child practice what to say to the bully so she will be prepared the next time.
- Seek help from your child's teacher or the school guidance counselor. Most bullying occurs on playgrounds, in lunchrooms and bathrooms, on school buses or in unsupervised halls. Ask the school administrators to find out about programs other schools

and communities have used to help combat bullying, such as peer mediation, conflict resolution, anger management training and increased adult supervision.

- Don't encourage your child to fight back. Instead, suggest that he or she try walking away to avoid the bully or seek help from a teacher, coach or other adult.
- Help your child practice being assertive. The simple act of insisting that the bully leave her alone may have a surprising effect.
- Encourage your child to be with friends when traveling back and forth from school, during shopping trips or on other outings. Bullies are less likely to pick on a child in a group.

Signs that your child is being bullied include a sudden reluctance to go to school or to ride the bus, a change in appetite or sleep patterns or complaints of stomachaches. Look for abrupt differences in behavior and ask questions. If you suspect your child may be the victim of bullying, ask her to tell you what's going on. Try to listen without getting upset, and make sure that you respond in a positive and accepting manner. Let your child know it's not her fault and that she did the right thing by telling you.

If your child becomes withdrawn, depressed or reluctant to go to school, or if you see a decline in school performance, additional consultation or intervention may be required. A child and adolescent psychiatrist or other mental health professional can help your child, your family and the school to develop a strategy to deal with the bullying. Seeking professional assistance early can lessen the risk of lasting emotional consequences for your child.

Photo courtesy of Lynn Oliver

Chapter 11

People of Color with Albinism

Children of color who have albinism face a unique challenge. They may be treated differently by their families and peer groups, and are often subject to more scrutiny and more comments than other children with albinism. While the advice and information in this book is applicable to all children with albinism, it is important to recognize that there may be additional issues that need to be addressed for children of color.

In addition, as a parent of color, you will face more difficulties than other parents of children with albinism. Unfortunately, the questions, stares and comments you may receive are common experiences for people of color with albinism. It is very normal to be upset by people's reactions, and to have a difficult time dealing with the diagnosis. It can be shocking to have a child who looks so different from you and your family, but your baby doesn't know he is any different. **All your baby needs to know is that you love him.**

This chapter addresses some of the issues involved in parenting a child of color with albinism. We hope to provide you with some advice and different perspectives, but the most important thing to remember is that you are not alone. NOAH families of color are a tight-knit group, and can provide you with information and support.

149

Early Diagnosis

Many children of color with albinism are diagnosed shortly after birth because of the difference in the color of their skin. However, parents are often given very little information about albinism when their child is diagnosed. Many medical professionals are unfamiliar with the condition, and often give information based on myths rather than on medical research. This leaves parents feeling helpless and confused at a very vulnerable time. In addition, you may also face unwanted attention or receive inappropriate comments from medical professionals because albinism is an unusual condition.

In the beginning, it can be difficult to handle your emotions surrounding your child's diagnosis. This is very normal. Not only are you worried about your child's health and development, but you may also be experiencing feelings of sadness, isolation and surprise. All of these feelings are compounded by the insensitive comments you hear on a regular basis about your baby's appearance. Not only do people ask, "Where did he get that white hair?" they also question, "Whose baby is that?" While these comments and questions can be hurtful, most often they arise out of ignorance, and a simple explanation will be sufficient to stop them.

Each parent will develop his or her own way to handle these situations. Sometimes you will feel like responding and explaining, sometimes you won't. Don't worry if you sometimes get mad or defensive – it happens to all parents. Just remember that your child will pick up on your attitude as he gets older, and will develop part of his sense of self-esteem from how you respond to these questions.

One of the biggest benefits of early diagnosis is that you can connect with other families in NOAH right away. **NOAH Rapid Responders can put you in touch with other families of color who have been in your situation.** This is the best way to gain perspective and get good advice. You may even get a few snappy answers to those rude questions.

Other possible benefits of an early diagnosis include the ability to begin early intervention services that much sooner and to take immediate steps to address your child's light sensitivity.

> "NOAH has been a lifesaver for parents of children with albinism and people of color with albinism. Being a part of NOAH was the only time I had ever been with people like me. It was like I was at home. People of color with albinism are often isolated and many may grow up never seeing anyone else who looks like them."
>
> Saundra Sanders
> Chicago, IL
> adult with albinism

Dealing with Family and Community

A strong sense of self-worth and a network of support are important for all people with albinism. In a community of color, this may be more difficult to develop because of the greater difference in appearance. The first step is to help your family accept the difference in your child. As much as possible, encourage your family to talk, ask questions and learn about albinism. Further, be prepared to educate your child's primary village. If your child feels accepted by his family and community, he will have a stronger sense of self-esteem.

Unfortunately, there may often be stares and negative comments, particularly from those who do not understand the condition. However, your reaction is of the utmost importance because your child is watching and listening.

> "People are naturally curious about things they don't understand . . . so help them understand. Not everyone will be receptive to knowledge about albinism, but the lasting implication for your child will be one of confidence and self-acceptance. You as a parent MUST control your reactions, because your child will naturally follow your lead. If you are constantly angry and defensive, your child will view albinism as a reason to be ashamed or afraid."
>
> Ja-Nae Epps
> Irmo, SC
> adult with albinism

Parents should also learn to take advantage of "teachable moments," when and where they feel comfortable. More visibility in the media can also help reduce the lack of knowledge.

Helping Your Child Develop a Strong Identity

Developing a strong identity is important for all children, but is imperative for children of color with albinism. So often, self-esteem is connected to personal appearance. Children of color with albinism may struggle with their appearance, as they don't quite "fit in" with those around them. If possible, attend a NOAH conference or find a child of color in your area with albinism. We can't stress enough the benefits for your child of interacting with other kids of color with albinism. It will greatly reduce his sense of isolation and difference.

Teach your child, with examples, that people of color come in a plethora of shades, all beautiful. Teach him, from a young age, that he is beautiful and that his features are unique. Teach him to be proud of who he his is and to walk tall with confidence.

Photo courtesy of Positive Exposure, Rick Guidotti

"I am an African-American mother of a boy who is full of life and energy. His entry into our lives was quite a surprise, as Nicholas was born with oculocutaneous albinism. When he arrived, his father and I were unfamiliar with albinism and what it entailed. We had no idea that this condition was part of our family's genetic make-up. I later found out, through my mother, that I had several cousins on her side of the family with albinism. While growing up, I rarely saw individuals in my community with albinism. So, when I found myself on the labor and delivery table with my baby in my arms, looking at his white skin, white hair and gray eyes, I was quite surprised – to say the least.

As a new parent without substantial knowledge of albinism, I felt frustrated by the hospital staff's lack of knowledge as well. I was told that most black babies came out with light skin and so my son's skin tone would darken as time progressed. I was, however, still puzzled by his white hair and light eyes. After talking to my mother, she was the first person to suggest to me that he had albinism, based on our family history. Still bewildered, I went back to the physicians and implored them to verify whether he had albinism. Because they were not sure of the criteria for the diagnosis, they eventually referred me to a geneticist, who after a comprehensive evaluation formally diagnosed my son with this condition. I felt somewhat relieved once I was told about albinism because at least my son's condition was no longer an unknown.

Dealing with the lack of knowledge of albinism within the medical profession, as well as within the circle of my family and friends, was only one of my difficulties as an African American mother. Unfortunately, I have had to deal with the insensitivity of others, starting at the time of my son's birth. As my son entered the world, my obstetrician stated aloud to everyone in the delivery room, "Someone must have been messing around with the mailman." I had no idea why she had said such a thing, until I actually saw what my baby looked like. I realized that this was her attempt at humor. Unfortunately, it was my first (and not last) encounter with the insensitivity of others in the years that followed.

There have been several occasions when my family has been out to dinner and someone has come up and asked us if that was our child. Even after we responded, they would still continue to question us about his parentage. On another occasion, while shopping in the mall with my infant son, the store clerk asked if I was babysitting. At other times, I've been asked if I was a foster mother, as well as being asked if I adopted him. I've also been told by other women of color that my baby was cute, but I "needed to get him a tan." One woman stated that "he was cute, but I needed to stick with my own kind."

Whether the insensitive comments were intentional or came from ignorance about albinism, in the end they did not feel good. And although my baby was young, I did not want him to be subjected to such insensitivity, which he himself would eventually face as he matured.

Thereafter, I felt a strong need to educate myself on albinism, so that in the long run I could educate others around me on the condition, and most importantly, so that I could feel confident when faced with insensitivity. I researched albinism and was referred to NOAH by our early intervention vision teacher. NOAH has been such a support to us. Through NOAH, we have had the opportunity to meet other parents and to share our experiences of raising a child with albinism. Most importantly, our participation has exposed my son to other children with albinism. As my son matured, he became more aware of his difference from other children and began to feel that he was the only one in the world with albinism since he had not seen others in his family, school, church and in our overall community with this condition. Because of his promptings and requests to meet other people with albinism, we attended our first NOAH conference when he was six years old. Undoubtedly, this was the best thing that we could have done for him because it gave him a sense of pride, security and belonging.

As a parent of a child with albinism, I offer the following advice, not only to other parents of color, but to all parents raising a child with albinism:

• Educate yourself and obtain as much information as you can about albinism. Unless you are aware that albinism may be a part of your genetic make-up, recognize that it will be a surprise to have a baby with albinism.

• Be prepared and ready to share your knowledge with others, including family members, teachers and strangers. Your child will be comfortable with having albinism if he sees that you are comfortable in talking about it.

• Join NOAH. Attend its conferences and/or events. It's a great way to meet other people with similar experiences and it lets your child see and know that he is not the only one in the world with albinism.

• Help your child to understand albinism and not to be ashamed of it. You want your child to ultimately accept himself without needing approval from others. Encourage your child to express his feelings and experiences in dealing with albinism.

• Help your child to develop strong self-esteem. A child with albinism should have a strong sense of who he is as a person and should know he is accepted by his family. Focus on your child's strengths and help to nurture his interests.

• Last, but not least, tell your child that you love him as often as you can. A child with albinism, or any child in general, needs to feel loved and supported in his family.

My son, Nicholas, continues to surprise us with his charming personality. He is engaging and is quite a character. Although Nicholas may have low vision, he does well in school, and enjoys martial arts, swimming and scouts. He likes creating science experiments at home, playing video games and is a typical boy who enjoys scaring his mother with toy bugs.

"

Garcia Lee
Waldorf, MD
parent of a child with albinism

Photo courtesy of Positive Exposure, Rick Guidotti

Chapter 12

Sun Safety

Children with albinism must develop good sun safety habits at a young age, not only for comfort, but also for the health of their eyes and skin. According to the American Academy of Dermatology, approximately 80 percent of unsafe sun exposure and potential skin damage occurs before the age of eighteen. One serious sunburn and/or blistering can increase your chance of developing skin cancer by as much as 50 percent.

As parents, you can help your child create healthy lifelong patterns by making sun safety a family habit, regardless of each individual's level pigment: everyone wears sunscreen, hats and sunglasses. This chapter provides an overview of the most important sun-safety rules, and gives you practical tips on how to apply them to your family. With simple sun-safe habits, your child can thrive outside.

Sunscreen

Sunscreen application will be a daily part of your child's life, so it is important to always have the right sunscreen available and to know how and when to apply it to ensure full protection. Most people don't use enough sunscreen, don't reapply it often enough, and don't use it year-round. The American Cancer Society stresses that everyone should wear sunscreen all year, even on cloudy days. Harmful UVA rays are present during all daylight hours, can travel through glass and clouds, and reflect off of snow, water and concrete.

Photo courtesy of Susan Leslie DuBois

157

On any day that you or your child is going to be outside for more than a very short time, you should follow these sun-safety rules:

- Use a sunscreen of at least SPF 30.
- Apply a generous amount (about a palmful) thirty minutes before going outside.
- Reapply sunscreen every ninety minutes or after swimming, towel drying or perspiring, even if the label says the product is waterproof.

The Difference between UVA and UVB Rays

Sunlight consists of two types of harmful rays – UVA and UVB rays. The UVB rays are the primary cause of sunburn and skin cancer, and are blocked by simple window glass. That's why you don't get sunburned while riding in the car when the windows are rolled up. UVA rays do pass through window glass and penetrate deeper into the dermis, or base layer of the skin. They also contribute to sunburns and skin cancer, which is why it is important to make sure you get a sunscreen that is labeled "broad spectrum," with ingredients that also screen UVA rays, such as benzophenone, oxybenzone, sulisobenzone, titanium dioxide, zinc oxide, and avobenzone.

Sunscreen's SPF

SPF stands for sun protection factor, and is indicated by a number that can range from as low as two to greater than fifty. The higher the number, the greater the product's ability to deflect the sun's burning rays. SPF numbers refer to how long it takes for someone wearing one full ounce of sunscreen to sunburn under a standard ultraviolet lamp, compared with the time in which that person would burn without any sunscreen. In theory, if a person wearing no sunscreen could stay in the sun ten minutes without burning, he or she could wear an SPF 20 sunscreen and stay in the sun twenty times that ten minutes, or 200 minutes, before burning.

SPF protection does not actually increase proportionately with a designated SPF number. A sunscreen with SPF 15 protects against 93 percent of harmful UV rays, SPF 30 protects against 97 percent, and SPF 50 protects against 98 percent of the harmful rays.

While most health care providers and organizations recommend an SPF of at least fifteen for adequate sun protection, It is prudent for people with albinism to use maximum skin protection by using sun block rated at least SPF 30. While the type of sunscreen you choose is based on individual preference, using a very high SPF number is not as important as proper application and continued reapplication.

Getting the Sunscreen onto Your Kid

The American Academy of Dermatology recommends that infants under six months of age be kept out of direct sun, and covered by protective clothing. It is generally accepted that you can apply sunscreen beginning at six months of age, but that small amounts of chemical–free sunscreens are safe for younger babies with albinism. Sunscreens with zinc oxide or titanium dioxide are considered "chemical-free" sunscreens, and are good for young children and high-risk areas such as the nose, lips, and shoulders.

To get your young child not only accustomed to sunscreen but enthusiastic about applying it, make it fun! Play "connect the dots" by placing dots of sunscreen on your child's body, and have her connect the dots by rubbing it in. Have your child apply the sunscreen herself with adult supervision, or let her put sunscreen on you. You could incorporate a massage with the application of sunscreen for younger children. Be sure to help your child to ensure adequate coverage and make sure she washes her hands afterwards to keep her from touching sunscreen-covered hands to her eyes.

The application of sunscreen should be a regular part of your family's morning routine. It can be just another step in the "get dressed, eat breakfast, brush hair, brush teeth, put on sunscreen" regimen. Keep extra sunscreen in the car, at work and at your child's school for those times when you forget to apply it. You can even keep a small tube in your older child's backpack.

This health routine must also extend to your child's school or other care providers. In some cases, you may need to sign a medical statement or have your pediatrician write a "prescription" that will require care providers to apply sunscreen to your child. For the child with albinism, sun protection is a medical issue, and the regular application of sunscreen is just as important as other routine medical care.

Sunburn Happens

While we all strive to be safe with our children in the sun, just about every kid – with albinism or without – will get a sunburn at some point. Do not beat yourself up over it! Do the best that you can to protect your child, and have aloe gel and lollipops on hand for those rare circumstances when your child gets too much sun.

Sun Protective Clothing

All clothing has an SPF, so it can play an important role in keeping your child comfortable and safe while outside. For example, a basic, white cotton T-shirt has an SPF of seven, while a long-sleeved, dark denim shirt has an estimated SPF of 1,700. In general, clothing made of tightly woven fabric offers the most protection from the sun. Woven fabrics that have see-through holes between individual threads allow UV rays to penetrate through to the skin and are not recommended for sun protection.

In addition, clothing may be treated with a laundry rinse that increases its SPF. You may choose to purchase clothing already treated to have a high SPF. However, given how quickly children grow, you may prefer a commercially available, do-it-yourself laundry rinse that can turn any item of clothing or material into a sun-protective garment. Please see the Resource section of this book for more information.

You can wash towels and beach cover-ups in an SPF rinse, too. Try washing old sheets with the rinse and then use them to make a backyard tent or to drape over a stroller or playpen.

Sunglasses

Sunglasses are important for children with albinism for several reasons. Many children with albinism are photophobic, and sunglasses make them comfortable while outside. However, sunglasses are also extremely important for the health and safety of their eyes. Exposure to UVA and UVB rays can damage delicate eye tissue and harm vision. In addition, UVB damage to the eyes is cumulative, and can lead to long-term diseases of the eye, such as cataracts and cancer. For this reason, it is important to teach your child to wear sunglasses, even if she is not particularly light sensitive.

Look for sunglasses that block 99 percent of UVA and UVB rays and are a comfortable fit for your child. Those that fit snugly to the face, like wrap-style sunglasses, will also prevent light from entering from the sides and will reduce glare. Let your child help determine how dark the lenses should be, and don't worry if they don't seem dark enough. Dark-colored sunglasses don't provide better protection from UV rays. A chemical coating applied to the lens provides UV protection, not the lens color.

Photo courtesy of Susan Leslie DuBois

Another option is a pair of sunglasses with photochromic lenses that get darker when exposed to sunlight. However, these lenses are chemically treated to react to UV light, and will not darken in a car. A benefit of photochromic lenses is that they can be made with your child's eyeglass prescription, which means you might have one less pair of glasses to keep track of. Some photochromic lenses do not darken quickly enough when going from indoors to outdoors; others are adequate. Again, personal preference and lifestyle should be your guide when selecting sunglasses and lenses. You can find a wide variety of sunglasses for babies and young children in stores, as well as online. Work with your low vision specialist or optician to determine the best option for your child.

Tinted Windows

Another easy and effective way to accommodate your child's light sensitivity is to tint the windows of your car. You can purchase a roll of static cling window film online, or at most automobile supply stores, and install it yourself. Or you can take your car to an auto detailer with tinting experience. Tinted windows let in significantly less light, and also reduce the impact of glare. Look for tints that block 99 percent of UV rays for the best protection. See the Resources section of the book for more information. Remember to check with your state to see what levels of tint are acceptable, or whether you need a special permit to darken your windows due to your child's medical condition. For a list of state laws regarding acceptable levels of tint in car windows, see **www.tintcenter. com/laws**.

You can apply the extra tint film to windows in your house that are not conducive to curtains or shades, or even to that pesky skylight. Can't find swim goggles or sunglasses that are dark enough? Make a template of the lens, and cut a piece of the film to fit!

Portable Shade

An inexpensive, pop-up sunshade for outdoor use is a great investment because it will increase your flexibility and safety while outside. Shades vary in size, but their portability is the key to their usefulness. Look for something that folds up and is easy to carry. Zip-down windows and flaps are helpful, too.

Some shades are designed specifically for the beach, with side pockets to fill with sand instead of stakes. Shades are also handy for sunny playgrounds, picnics and backyard play dates. Kids view them as cool tents rather than as a sun-safety measure. Portable shades are particularly useful for napping babies and toddlers, and can be a great way to allow a parent to spend time outdoors too.

Other Considerations

The National Weather Service predicts UV risk on a scale of one (low) to ten (high) for many communities, factoring in their altitude, the angle of the sun at noon there, and the anticipated cloud cover. Here are some ways these factors come into play:

- Latitude: A person who can tolerate one hour of sun in Florida without burning can tolerate two hours of sun in New Jersey under the same conditions.
- Season: The greatest intensity of ultraviolet light occurs at the summer solstice, on about June 22. Ultraviolet intensity on May 1 is the same as on August 15.
- Altitude: Each 1,000-foot increase in altitude adds four percent to the intensity of the rays that cause sunburn. The intensity of sunlight at 5,000 feet elevation is about 20 percent greater than at sea level.
- Weather: On a bright day with a thin cloud cover we are exposed to 60 percent to 80 percent of the ultraviolet rays that are present on a clear day. Clouds can cool temperatures and create a false impression that there is little risk of sunburn

Chapter 13

Your Child in the Classroom

Few issues raise as many concerns as the proper educational atmosphere for your child. Whether your child's first experience is a daycare room at three months old, or a kindergarten classroom at five years old, there are some important considerations to keep in mind for your low vision child. This chapter outlines some of these issues, and provides you with some tips on navigating the school setting.

As a partner in your child's education, you must be open and honest with the staff of the program about albinism and how it will impact your child in the classroom or daycare setting. Work together with the staff to provide a safe, fun and enriching environment for your child.

Choosing the Right Program

Selecting an appropriate atmosphere for your baby, toddler or school-age child is a tough job, whether he has albinism or not. Only you know your child's unique personality and can best assess the type of environment in which he will thrive. Children with low vision may have difficulty in a setting that is loud, large and very stimulating. Since this describes many early educational environments, you will have to consider how these factors may impact your child. When assessing the physical environment of a daycare center or classroom, consider the following questions:

- Is the room brightly lit? Can some overhead lights be turned off?
- Are there large windows? Are there curtains or blinds that can be lowered?

- Are there open, uncluttered play spaces so your child can easily navigate the room?
- Can wall charts and other wall materials easily be moved down to accommodate your child's visual impairment?
- Is the classroom loud?
- Is there a highly patterned rug or play surface, which might be visually tiring or distracting?
- Is the playground shady?
- Are there changes in grade or a lot of steps in the classroom or on the playground?
- What time of day do the children typically go outside?

If you have concerns about the physical environment, ask the director or principal whether changes can be made to the classroom to accommodate your child. You can simply say, "My child is visually impaired and is light-sensitive. Would it be possible to lower the shades in here in the morning when the sun is bright?" Giving a brief description of the impact of albinism will also allow you to gauge how sensitive the staff or teacher will be to any issues that arise. The director or principal can then follow up with any further questions he or she has, and you will both be able to get a feeling for whether or not this is an appropriate placement for your child.

Most educators are very willing to take steps to ensure that your child will be comfortable in the classroom. For the public school student, some of these changes will be mandatory under your child's Individualized Education Program. An unwillingness to consider these minor changes is a good sign that the daycare or pre-school might not be the best place for your child. If you meet with resistance in the public school setting, get a note from your doctor and try to educate the staff about the impact of photophobia and low vision on your child.

If the physical environment is adaptable and acceptable, the next step is to assess the internal environment: the staff and the program. Once again, you know your child best, and you must use your own instinct when assessing potential placements. Note how the teachers and staff interact with the students, and ask how comfortable they are with applying sunscreen and helping to keep track of hats and glasses. Ask about the program or curriculum. Developing social skills and play skills are more important at young ages, and are often areas where low vision children need extra help.

Special Education and Pre-School

Many states or counties have special education pre-school classes that may be beneficial to the child with albinism. If your child is receiving early intervention services through the state, discuss this as an option with your service provider. Your child may benefit from more intensive services to help with gross and fine motor skills, and with developing appropriate social behaviors.

Some parents are concerned about labeling their child by placing him in a special education setting. Pre-school children don't understand labels, and many studies have shown that children with delays catch up faster when they receive targeted special education services.

Photo courtesy of Positive Exposure, Rick Guidotti

167

Preparing for School

Your child will probably be very excited to start school. There are several things you can do to help him transition to the new routine and to help him be comfortable in a new setting. Ask the director or principal if you can bring him in a few times before school starts, so you can begin to familiarize him with the classroom and the layout of the school. Make sure he knows how to get to the office and the bathroom. Also, familiarize him with the routine for getting home, whether he will ride the bus, walk or get a ride from a parent.

Take him to the school's playground on weekends so he is comfortable with the equipment. He will be better able to keep up with the other kids on the playground if he is familiar with the play structures. If you know any of the children that will be in his class, try to organize a few play dates beforehand, so he will start with a friend in the class.

> Socially, it may be difficult for the young child with albinism to keep track of fifteen friends and consistently match names to faces, especially when they move so quickly around the room! Our daughter had a hard time recognizing a friend with chin-length, very curly hair who showed up one day with all of her hair pulled on top of her head in a ponytail. You can enlist the teachers' help in this area by having the teacher give your child visual cues about his peers to help him better recognize his friends ("Oh, look, Sophie is wearing a ponytail in her hair today!" or "I see Jake is wearing a red shirt!" or "Michael is playing with the big blue truck.") When games are played or songs are sung in a large group, naming children ("Mimi's wearing a green shirt, green shirt, green shirt...") may also be helpful.
>
> Randi Ostrove
> Highland Park, NJ
> parent of a child with albinism

Sharing Information

When choosing a daycare or school setting, it is important to create a dialogue with the director of the program and potential teachers. Some parents may be reluctant to disclose the fact that their child has albinism due to a fear of misconceptions or maltreatment on the part of the staff. Other parents may decide that this information is unnecessary because they don't feel that the albinism will have an impact on the daily routine of the program. This is a difficult issue. Your child may not seem light

Photo courtesy of Lynn Oliver

sensitive or developmentally delayed in any way. However, from circle time to story hour to the physical environment of the classroom and the playground, addressing certain factors will help your low vision child. Your child will gain much more from an environment in which he can fully participate. Sharing the information will help your child to have the most enriching education experience possible.

Explain in simple terms that your child is visually impaired, and give examples to the best of your ability. A teacher will be much less concerned if he or she knows your child will be able to see the materials – even if he needs to hold them up close. While each child's needs are different, you might say, "My child has a visual impairment due to albinism. His day-to-day functioning is not particularly affected by this and he looks and acts pretty much like your typical two-year old. But he may need to sit closer to the teacher during stories and it might be helpful for a teacher to assist him on the playground at first until he gets comfortable with the equipment."

You should also provide an explanation as to the level of your child's light sensitivity and explain that he will need to have a hat, sunglasses and sunscreen on for outside playtime. You may wish to share a recent evaluation from early intervention services, as well as a current report from the pediatric ophthalmologist, and informational pamphlets from NOAH. For those children entering kindergarten, an IEP should already be in the works. This provides an excellent vehicle for sharing information with the school.

In addition, you can create a document yourself, and in the case of an older child, with his help. This can take the form of a short, one-page explanation about albinism and how it impacts your child. The short explanation will also be handy for after-school programs, summer camps and organized sports. The following can be used as a guide to help you decide what information you wish to share:

Information about "Zachary Jones"

Zach has albinism, which is a genetic condition that results in (reduced or a lack of) pigment his eyes, skin and hair. He has a slight delay in _____, but is typically developing in all other ways.

Zachary is visually impaired. He has difficulty seeing detail and may need to look closely at small objects and books. He follows a picture book and loves to run on the playground and watch TV. During circle time and other small group activities, he can participate more fully if he is allowed to get close enough to the book or object to make up for his visual impairment.

Zachary wears prescription eyeglasses, and should have them on at all times while _____. Exceptions to this include _____.

Zach is sensitive to bright light and glare, and needs _____. Please allow him to wear a hat inside if the room is too bright, and when no other accommodations can be made.

Before Zach goes outside, he must have sunscreen applied to all exposed areas of his skin. When he is outside, he must wear his sunglasses and a hat.

When his eyes are bothering him, you might notice _____. He should be allowed to take a break.

Please remember to ask if he needs to see something up close – he may forget to ask! Also, please leave a copy of this information with any substitute teachers.

It may be helpful to schedule a meeting with the teacher and staff before school starts. All the educators who will work with your child need to understand the nature of his visual impairment. This will give you an opportunity to educate the team about your child, and answer any preliminary questions they have about albinism. For example, it is important that the gym teacher knows to modify the way she gives direction to your child. For instance, rather than saying "kick the ball towards the goal", the teacher should say "kick the ball towards the goal, which is straight ahead of you (or to the left)". Make sure the art teacher doesn't seat him by a window, or hang his work up high where he can't see it. And ask the librarian to seat your child close during story time.

Once the staff has all this information and gets to know your child, they will undoubtedly have questions as to what they can and should be doing for him at school to create the best possible environment. After two weeks, ask for an informal meeting to answer any questions the staff might have, and to assess how your child is doing in the classroom.

Hats, Glasses & Lotion – The Triple Play

You must also educate the staff about sun safety and skin care for your child. The staff will likely prefer that you apply sunscreen before your child leaves home in the morning, and then they will reapply sunscreen before your child goes outside during the school day. Because the Food and Drug Administration (FDA) classifies sunscreen as a drug, you may have to provide a medical permission slip authorizing school staff to apply it to your child. This is no different from the instructions from parents whose children have prescription medications or food allergies, and should be treated with the same level of care and respect.

Leave an extra set of sunglasses and some hats in your child's cubby, for those days when he forgets to bring something. If you have tricks for helping your child to keep his hat or sunglasses on, share these with the staff. Also, let the staff know whether it is okay for your child to take his hat off once in a while when playing outside. In a short time, the teachers and staff will be very accustomed to the things your child needs to feel comfortable in his classroom.

Make a sign for your child's cubby with a picture of a hat, a pair of sunglasses and sunscreen on it. Not only will this serve as a reminder to the teachers, it will begin to plant the seeds of self-reliance in your child.

Classroom Modifications

Whether your child is in an infant program at a daycare facility or a kindergarten class at an elementary school, the design of the room he is in will affect his comfort and behavior. If your child is especially sensitive to light, ask the staff to lower the shades at a particular time of day or to seat your child with his back to the windows during circle time. Many classrooms have two or more sets of fluorescent overhead lights. One can be turned off to accommodate your child without impacting the other kids.

When your child begins a new program, ask the teacher to give him a tour of the room and show him where to find everything he will need for a successful school day: tissues, smocks, the bathroom, the garbage can, books, paper and crayons. The teacher will need to repeat this process if he or she changes the classroom's physical set-up, because a child with a visual impairment may function in his space by learning the physical layout of the classroom, rather than by "seeing" it.

Moving things around frequently may make the classroom harder to navigate for a child with a visual impairment. If the blocks are always on the block shelf, dolls are always in their cribs in the housekeeping area, and crayons are always in the red bin on the art shelf, this will help the young child with albinism to function more independently in the classroom. If you take your child in each morning, look to see if anything is different about the layout of the classroom and point out any changes to your child.

You can play a game with your child to see if he can figure out what is different about the classroom. Or you can send him on a treasure hunt by giving him clues about what is different, and letting him use his visual skills to figure it out.

In any early childhood program, artwork and charts should be hung on the wall at the children's eye level. This is especially important to allow a young child with albinism to fully participate in classroom activities. If charts or signs are used in the classroom for circle time, attendance, the daily schedule or classroom helpers, they should be hung low on the walls, and be clearly written in a dark color.

The size of the print in books may not be an issue at this age since most fonts in children's picture books are quite large, but you should ask your child's teacher to be aware of the issue. Worksheets should be clear and dark, and if the children are going to cut out figures, it can be helpful for the teacher to outline the image in heavy magic marker.

Your child should be permitted to sit as close to the teacher as is necessary during story time or during other group activities in which he needs to see what the teacher is doing (finger plays, felt board stories, puppet shows). It may even be helpful if your child is permitted to become familiar with the book or materials before the activity begins so that he is better able to follow along visually during the activity.

> When Sophie was in Pre-K, one day, she had a substitute teacher. Her regular teacher had not left a note regarding Sophie's needs in the classroom but I happened to be volunteering in the classroom that day. The substitute teacher had all the children sit around the perimeter of the carpet and she began to read a book to them. I stood back and noticed that Sophie was sitting pretty far away. Before I could step in, Sophie called out, "I need to sit closer." The substitute asked, "Why?", perhaps thinking that here's one of those kids who always wants attention. Sophie said, clearly, "My eyes don't work like everyone else's because I have albinism." The substitute looked surprised by how clearly this was articulated by a four year old and agreed that she could certainly move closer. It was an extremely proud moment for me, to see firsthand, my daughter acting as her own best advocate without my intervention needed. It also showed me that while communication between home and school is key in getting our children's needs met, we need to be sure to teach our children to advocate for themselves and the appropriate way to communicate their own needs when we are not there to intervene.
>
> Randi Ostrove
> Highland Park, NJ
> parent of a child with albinism

Make sure your child has appropriate school supplies. Children with low vision often have trouble seeing their writing if they use pencils with number two lead. Have your child try a number three pencil with harder lead or a wider artist's pencil. Short, wide washable markers are great for little hands to hold, and dark lines on the writing paper will be easier for your child to follow. Glue that has a tint until it dries will be easier for your child to see. A vision teacher can give you additional suggestions about supplies for children with low vision.

Many schools have a television set in the room for movies and school broadcasts. If possible, make sure the television is on a low cart or table. If it is suspended from the ceiling, it is unlikely that your child will derive much benefit from whatever is being shown. Also, if he will use a computer in class, make sure to enlarge the font, and slow down the mouse speed. These are easy settings to change on a computer, and will make it much easier for your child to use.

Many children with low vision have difficulty with depth perception and with negotiating uneven terrain. Jungle gyms and play sets can be tough because they present different walking surfaces and changes in grade and steps. Children move from asphalt to rubberized surface to wood chips on a typical playground. Those transitions are challenging for someone who is sensitive to glare and has low vision. Share this information with the staff and let them know your child needs their support in this area. Verbal cues are a great way to help your child navigate an unfamiliar play set.

Addressing Problems

Teachers and staff need to be aware that the child with albinism may be over-stimulated or overwhelmed in the typical pre-school classroom due to bright light, noise and the activity level. This could result in externalizing behaviors (such as "acting out") or internalizing behaviors (such as playing alone). There are also physical responses that signal eye fatigue or exposure to too much light. If your child is squinting, has a hand over his eyes, has increased nystagmus or seems to physically withdraw, the teacher must respond. He or she should know what to do: turn down the lights or the music, allow your child to take break from the classroom by going for a short walk in a quiet hallway, or help your child to engage in a more appropriate activity.

All children will have difficulty in school or daycare at some point. While you should be careful not to overcompensate for your child's condition; when problems arise, consider whether albinism is a contributing factor. For example, if your child is being disruptive during story time, is he having difficulty seeing the material? If he doesn't want to play on the playground, is it because it is too bright? If he doesn't like to do table work, think about the physical environment. He made need more frequent breaks from close work. If he is having trouble with his peers, it may be related to an inability to read facial expressions. Not everything will be related to his albinism, but it should certainly factor into your discussion of the situation.

You and your child's teacher must strike a delicate balance between accounting for the effects of albinism, and excusing poor behavior. No one wants to see his or her child struggle with behavior issues, but you can't blame everything on the albinism. Nor can you lose sight of who your child is as an individual and what his needs really are. If he is not especially sensitive to light, there is no need for the school to turn down the lights or close the curtains. If he seems to be able to read the print on his nametag just fine, there is no need for the teacher to make the print any larger. If he always refuses to keep a hat on during outdoor play at school but always has sunscreen on and wears his sunglasses, let it go.

One of the most important things to remember is that all children with albinism are different, just as all children without albinism are different. Like any other parent, you are the best advocate for your child, and you need to be sure his individual needs are being met. If you believe your child is not receiving the services he really needs, speak up. If you are not comfortable with the program you have chosen, look elsewhere, or work with the teachers to create a better atmosphere.

Evaluations and Tests

Most children with albinism will be evaluated to determine whether they need any services, and all children are tested in kindergarten to measure baseline skills. It is critically important for all test administrators to work with a teacher of the visually impaired (TVI) in modifying your child's assessment, ensuring accommodations are made and interpreting the results.

If a TVI is unavailable in your area, ask to work with an O&M specialist. An occupational therapist can also help ensure that the necessary accommodations are made for a child with albinism. You should have at least one of these specialists fully familiar with your child and his needs in your school system. The specialist (preferably a TVI) will have detailed information on your child, the impact of albinism on his vision, and a clear understanding of how to modify the testing and classroom environment.

With the proper supportive environment, children with albinism should do as well as their typically-sighted peers on standardized tests.

Keep in mind that just as any group of children demonstrates a wide range of abilities, so too will any group of children with albinism. Parents or educators may miss certain learning disabilities because they overemphasize the impact of albinism on performance. However, some tests will present additional difficulties for a child with a visual impairment, so it is best to ask questions about all measurement tests given to your child, and ensure that appropriate modifications or accommodations are made during the testing process.

One common assessment is the Wechsler Intelligence Scale for Children (WISC), Verbal Comprehension Scale, which tests intelligence through six language-based sections and seven visual-motor sections. It is given to children ages six to sixteen. This and other cognitive assessments include some sections that are timed, to measure quickness of completion. Timed sections may be difficult for a child with low vision because it takes him longer to analyze visual data, and he may be impacted by visual fatigue. As such, timed tests are often extended to one and one-half times the normal allotted times for children with visual impairments.

Children with low vision often cannot analyze information and perform visual discrimination at the same rate as typically-sighted children. They simply lack the tools. Thus timed tests should not be used as the sole measure of your child's abilities, and accommodations such as extended testing time should be provided. However, the results from these exams should not be discounted entirely, as they can help identify appropriate modifications for the classroom. Your job is to be sure the final test report includes language explaining your child's physical circumstances. For example:

"These results of this test should be interpreted with the knowledge that Jon has low vision and photophobia, which was not taken into account when scoring the exam. His performance was impacted by the small typeface and low contrast of the pictures. Also, he required additional time to process the highly visual information. The following accommodations were made to improve Jon's access to the test material: _____."

Ask your school officials early in the academic year for a schedule of all standardized tests and assessments your child will take. This will give you ample time to work with a TVI or other specialist to develop the necessary accommodations. Testing accommodations should be documented and included in your child's IEP. In some cases, your school may need to apply to the state or other testing organization for specific accommodations for your child.

If you lack the assistance of a specialist, you will have to familiarize the tester with the impact of low vision, photophobia and light sensitivity on your child. You should consider the following issues:

- Are there any low vision devices that would be helpful and appropriate?
- Is the lighting appropriate?
- Does you child have a suitable writing implement?
- Are test materials available in an accessible format (such as large print, audio/narrated or tactile)?
- Are any materials laminated? (Laminated materials increase glare; materials protected in a matte finish contact paper are more low vision-friendly.)
- Is the examiner aware that your child may need to hold test items close?
- Does the test include timed tasks that require children to shift their gaze from a visual stimulus to other test materials? A child working at a close distance may have difficulty performing quickly. A lower score on this type of activity may reflect visual limitations, not a deficit in the skill being tested. Consider the option of extended testing times.
- Does the test include machine-scored bubble paper or a Scranton sheet for answers? Children with low vision and nystagmus will have great difficulty in lining up the letters, numbers and bubbles, and should not be expected to do this in a testing environment. One option is to have a teacher or aide transfer your child's answers from a test booklet to the answer sheet.
- Is a qualified teacher of the visually impaired available to consult with the examiner and assist with selecting appropriate tests, adapting materials, administering the assessment and interpreting the results?

Photo courtesy of Positive Exposure, Rick Guidotti

Reading Strategies

It is never too early to start reading to your child on a regular basis. Reading to your child, and later with your child, will give you cozy time together and may even help develop a lifelong reader. In addition, it will provide insight into your child's reading and reasoning capabilities. Ask questions and encourage your child to be inquisitive too. That will teach him to ask questions himself while he is reading, which helps foster better comprehension.

Children with low vision will learn to read like any typically-sighted child, but will hold the book closer, and may have difficulty tracking the words on the page. There are several things you can do to help establish early literacy, and to promote healthy reading habits.

The most important thing you can do to promote reading skills is to read to your child every day. Even when your child is too young to understand the words, your tone of voice and the physical contact are important, and will help foster a love of reading. Choose books with simple pictures and look for rhyming patterns. Learning to rhyme is an early reading skill, and it doesn't require good vision. Young children love

179

flap books, and manipulating the flaps will help to build their visual attention, increase fine motor skills and reward them for using visual skills. For older toddlers, play reading games that build on your child's strong auditory skills by asking questions that test comprehension, such as, "Where did that silly cat go?"

When your child is a little older, you can encourage comprehension and good visual skills by looking at the book's pictures together first and asking questions that require visual decoding and scanning, such as "Where is the puppy?" or "What face is the little girl making?" and "Why is she making that face?" Responding to these questions helps train your child to rely on her visual skills, as kids with low vision often use their excellent auditory skills to garner information from a story.

When preparing your pre-schooler to learn to read, work on the left-to-right progression skill. He needs this because we read English from the left side of the page to the right. Any games that begin from the left and go to the right are helpful. One way to reinforce this skill is to work on stringing beads. Have your child grasp a pipe cleaner in his right hand, and a large wooden bead in the left (both items are widely available in craft stores). A pipe cleaner is easier for a young child to work with than a shoelace or piece of string. Help your child pick patterns of beads, such alternating size or color. This will help him learn left-to-right progression, but will also reinforce fine motor skills. Another way to practice this is with a simple bean bag toss game. You will need a bean bag and a row of shoe boxes. Have your child start by standing a foot or two from the box on the left, and work at tossing in the beanbag. When he gets it in, he moves to the next box to the right. If your child misses one of the boxes, have him start from the beginning, and repeat the process. These simple games will help strengthen his brain's ability to process information, recognize patterns and move in a left-to-right progression.

Once your child is reading, you may notice that he has some difficulty keeping his place on the page. This is not uncommon for children with low vision or nystagmus. Fortunately, people with albinism have good contrast vision, which is what allows one to see a dime on the kitchen floor, or a piece of cereal on a high-chair tray. A plastic colored strip that provides contrast for a line of text can help your child focus on one line at time, reduce glare and maximize visual contrast.

Another tool is a "takistascope", which is simply a piece of dark plastic, cardboard or poster board with a slit or window cut out that is the size of a line of print. When your child places it over the page, it blocks out everything but the sentence your child is trying to read. Either of these tools can be made at home, and can be useful in helping your child to reduce visual clutter on a page so that he may focus more easily.

Your child's TVI or the school's reading specialist should be able to help you identify other strategies to help your child become a successful reader, but these are some simple ideas that will get you started.

Reading Resources

Audio books are a wonderful tool for children with a visual impairment, and can be very helpful in later school years. There are several excellent resources for audio books and school books for children. The National Library Service (NLS) offers free audio material, Braille and books on tape for school-age children, and Recording for the Blind & Dyslexic is the leading producer of educational materials for children with a visual impairment. Please see the Resource section for more information.

Chapter 14

Sports and the Child with Albinism

Parents should encourage their child with albinism to participate in individual and team sports from an early age – for all the same reasons they would encourage any child to do so: to learn good sportsmanship and fairness, to foster social interaction, to boost a child's self-confidence and to begin to teach the importance of exercise in maintaining a healthy lifestyle.

As a parent, you may be concerned about your child's ability to fully participate in sports, but the important thing to remember is to let your child set her own limits. Don't assume she won't be able to play soccer or T-ball, or that she won't enjoy it. In fact, preconceived notions are possibly the biggest obstacle your child will face with respect to sports and physical activities.

Many leagues have teams for children as young as four years old, and emphasize participation and sportsmanship rather than keeping score and promoting competition. This chapter outlines some of the issues you will encounter when considering sports for your child.

Choosing a Sport

Let your child sample a variety of different sports, but from the beginning, stress the importance of team skills. A child with low vision and photophobia may have more success with a "large ball" sport, such as soccer or basketball. To teach your child how to track a ball in the air

Photo courtesy of the Bergman Family

to catch it, start with a balloon, an inflatable beach ball or a large foam discs that won't hurt if she misses catching it. You can also wrap a ball in double-sided tape so your child will be less likely to drop it, or look for highly textured balls.

If your child does choose a "small ball" sport like baseball or T-ball, use a brightly colored ball, which will be easier for your child to see. Neon-colored balls are popular in some places, but if you can't find one, make your own using a can of brightly colored spray paint. You can also highlight boundary lines with neon landscaping paint. Shorten the baselines at first, to orient base runners. You can gradually lengthen the distance as your child gets used to running bases.

Golf can be a fun activity because much of it is done within three feet of the ball, and there's no running around chasing anyone. Start your child with a hollow plastic ball instead of a golf ball, which will be easier for her to track and won't travel as far. Use an orange emergency cone to mark the hole or cup. For putting practice, you can even spray paint around the hole to highlight it.

Many children with albinism gravitate toward individual sports like swimming, gymnastics, track or martial arts. These sports may be easier to adapt for a low vision child, and can help increase coordination. Nonetheless, almost every sport or activity can be adapted to suit your child's abilities. The most important thing is to find something your child enjoys. You can use the NOAH website to find advice and share information about helping your child participate in a particular sport.

Practical Considerations

The best way to help your child succeed in any sport is to follow the suggestions discussed throughout the book. Look for sports played indoors or in the evenings. Help to create a supportive environment by discussing your child's vision with her coach. Make sure the coaches understand how albinism impacts your child. Volunteer to assist with the team, if you can.

Also, help your child practice her sport at home as much as you can – make it special family time. Working on specific skills over and over will help your child develop confidence and competence. Talk to your

Photo courtesy of Louise Martinheira; Photo by KJ Sikkema Photography

child before the practice or game and explain what is going to happen. In addition to explaining the rules, make sure your child understands where the goals and boundaries are located.

Remember that typically-sighted children will be able to orient themselves simply by glancing around. A child with low vision may need additional cues or tricks to become comfortable. Remind your child to look for her team's shirt color if she is confused, or to listen for directions from the coach.

> Our daughter Sophie participated in a soccer program for the first time at age five, and even though she had played before, she could not follow the ball as it moved quickly down the field and with other kids blocking the view. We told her, "If you're not sure where the ball is, look for the big crowd of kids, run to them and look down and chances are, you'll find the ball there." This seemed to help her to keep track of the ball, at least, when she wasn't picking grass or flowers or pretending to fly down the field like an airplane!
>
> Randi Ostrove
> Highland Park, NJ
> parent of a child with albinism

If your child ends up playing a sport that has her on the field during bright times of the day, consider investing in a pair of tinted prescription sports goggles. While these can be pricey, they may make your child more comfortable. Talk to your optician about different options, but make sure the lenses are shatterproof. Also, the right sun protective sports clothing will be a regular part of your child's uniform. See the Resources section for some options but be sure to look online and ask other parents through the NOAH online community.

> Sports are extremely important to me. As a younger kid, I played soccer on various town teams, and I swam in the summer and winter competitively. In high school I ran varsity cross country, swam on the swim team and ran spring track. Taking part in a sport is a great way to get involved with a group and learn valuable team-building skills. I believe that children with albinism can take part in sports of any kind, with the proper adaptations.
>
> Kristen Daley
> Medfield, MA
> young adult with albinism

Adaptive Sports Programs

Adaptive sports programs that seek to increase the participation of people with disabilities are growing in popularity across the country. These programs cover a wide range of sports, including skiing, snowboarding, skating, kayaking, sailing and horseback riding.

For example, Disabled Sports USA (**www.dsusa.org**) is a national organization that offers sports training to anyone with a permanent disability. Disabled Sports USA was founded in 1967 to assist disabled war veterans, and has broadened its mission to include sports training for people of all ages and ranges of disabilities, including visual impairments. The organization also sanctions and conducts competitions and training for the Paralympics Games. The United Sates Association of Blind Athletes (USABA), a Community Based Organization of the United States Olympic Committee, has reached more than 100,000 blind individuals. USABA has emerged as more than just a world-class trainer of blind athletes, it has become a champion of the abilities of Americans who are legally blind.

If your child shows an affinity for a particular sport, look to see if there is an adaptive program in your area. Many adaptive sports programs offer scholarships and have volunteer opportunities. Please see the Resources section for more information.

NOAH Family Camp

NOAH sponsors a summer camp for kids with albinism and their parents. The family camp provides an opportunity for children with albinism to participate in sports and recreational activities with kids just like them and their families. Look on the NOAH website for more information.

There are also several camps tailored specially for children with low vision. Please see the Resources section of the book for more information. Keep in mind that almost any summer camp can work for your child if you plan appropriately.

Photo courtesy of Linda Wood

Resources

The following organizations were used as resources when creating this book and provide information, products and/or services for people with albinism. Contact information and resources change frequently, so be sure to look for additional assistance when needed. Resources are published on the NOAH website (www.albinism.org) and are updated periodically. This is not intended to be a complete list or an endorsement of any specific commercial provider but is offered as an informational starting point.

General Information and Support
The National Organization for Albinism and Hypopigmentation (NOAH)
P.O. Box 959
East Hampstead, NH 03826-0959
800-473-2310
Website: www.albinism.org
Email: info@albinism.org
A support and advocacy group for people with albinism and for parents whose children have albinism

American Foundation for the Blind
2 Penn Plaza, Suite 1102
New York, NY 10121
Phone: 212-502-7600
Website: www.afb.org
Email: afbinfo@afb.net
A national nonprofit that expands possibilities for people with vision loss such as broader access to technology; elevated quality of information and tools for the professionals who serve people with vision loss; and promoting independent and healthy living for people with vision loss by providing relevant and timely resources

American Nystagmus Network (ANN)
303-D Beltline Place, #321
Decatur, AL 35603
Website: www.nystagmus.org
Provides information and support regarding nystagmus, an eye condition commonly associated with albinism

HPS Network Inc.
One South Road
Oyster Bay, NY 11771-1905
Phone: 800-789-9HPS
Website: www.hpsnetwork.org
Email: info@hpsnetwork.org
Provides support and information for people and families dealing with Hermansky-Pudlak Syndrome and related disorders such as Chediak-Higashi Syndrome

Lighthouse Guild

15 West 65th Street
New York, NY 10023
Phone: 800-284-4422
Website: www.lighthouseguild.org
Email: info@lighthouseguild.org
Provides vision and rehabilitation services to the visually impaired, offers clinical services, education, research and advocacy for people with low vision and blindness

National Association for Parents of Children with Visual Impairments (NAPVI)

Lighthouse Guild Attn: NAPVI
15 West 65th Street
New York, NY 10023
Phone: 800-562-6265
Website: www.lighthouseguild.org/programs-services/education/napvi
Email: napvi@lighthouseguild.org
Provides support and information, workshops and conferences for parents of the visually impaired, and is a great source for links to other groups and agencies

National Federation of the Blind

200 East Wells Street (at Jernigan Place)
Baltimore, MD 21230
Phone: 410-659-9314
Website: www.nfb.org
Works to improve blind people's lives through advocacy, education, research, technology and programs encouraging independence and self-confidence

Medical Resources
Academy for Certification of Vision Rehabilitation and EducationProfessionals (ACVREP)

Website: www.acvrep.org
Dedicated to meeting the needs of the vision services field and providing high-quality professional certification in the disciplines of low vision therapy, orientation and mobility, and vision rehabilitation therapy

American Academy of Dermatology

P.O. Box 4014
Schaumberg, IL 60618
Phone: 866-503-7546
Website:www.aad.org
Email: online form
With a membership of more than 17,000, it represents virtually all practicing dermatologists in the United States, as well as a growing number of international dermatologists

College of Optometrists in Vision Development

Phone: 330-995-0718
Website: www.covd.org
Email: info@covd.org
A nonprofit association of eye care professionals to offer state-of-the-art services in: behavioral and developmental vision care, vision therapy and visual rehabilitation

International Academy of Low Vision Specialists (IALVS)

Phone: 888-778-2030
Website: www.ialvs.com
Strives to enhance the quality of life, independence and safety of patients by designing, prescribing and dispensing the highest quality, optically advanced, hands-free low vision devices available

National Society of Genetic Counselors

Phone: (312) 321-6834
Website: www.nsgc.org
Email: nsgc@nsgc.org
Promotes the professional interests of genetic counselors and provides a network for professional communications

The Optometric Extension Program Foundation

Phone: 410-561-3791
Website: www.oepf.org
An international organization dedicated to the advancement of optometry through the gathering and dissemination of information on vision and the visual process

Government Resources, Early Intervention and Education Information

American Council of the Blind

2200 Wilson Blvd.
Suite 650
Arlington, VA 22201-3354
Phone: 800-424-8666; 202-467-5081
Website: www.acb.org
Email: info@acb.org
Provides support and information for parents of children who are blind or visually impaired, holds an annual conference, and publishes a newsletter

Association for Education and Rehabilitation of the Blind and Visually Impaired (AER)

1703 North Beauregard Street
Suite 440
Alexandria, VA 22311
Phone: 703-671-4500
Website: www.aerbvi.org
Email: aer@aerbvi.org
Develops and promotes professional excellence through support of those who provide services to people with visual impairments by providing professional support, publications, professional development, scholarships and advocacy

Division on Visual Impairment, Council for Exceptional Children (DVI/CEC)

Website: http://community.cec.sped.org/DVI/home/
Advance the education of individuals with visual impairments and promotes related educational, scientific and charitable purposes, assists and supports The Council for Exceptional Children (CEC)

The Hadley School for the Blind

700 Elm Street
Winnetka, IL 60093
Phone: 800-323-4238
Website: www.hadley.edu
Email: info@hadley.edu
Offers courses to people with low vision or blindness and to parents of children with low vision or blindness through distance learning programs, online or through the mail

Perkins School for the Blind
175 North Beacon Street
Watertown, MA 02472
Phone: 617-924-3434
Website: www.perkins.org
Email: info@Perkins.org
Produces a publications, workbooks
and instructional tools for families and
caregivers of people who are blind or
visually impaired

PRO-ED Inc.
8700 Shoal Creek Boulevard
Austin, TX 78757-6897
Phone: 800-897-3202; 512-451-3246
Website: www.proedinc.com
Email: info@proedinc.com
Publisher standardized tests
(assessments), books (resource and
reference texts), curricular and therapy
materials and professional journals

**The Texas School for the Blind and
Visually Impaired**
1100 West 45th Street
Austin, TX 78756
Phone: 800-872-5273
Website: www.tsbvi.edu
The special education school for
students who have a visual impairment is
a statewide resource to parents of these
children as well as the professionals who
serve them, and the website offers a
wide range of information and resources
on education issues, technology,
curriculum and publications

U. S. Department of Education
Website: http://idea.ed.gov
A "one-stop shop" for resources related
to IDEA and its implementing regulations

Books and Publications
American Foundation for the Blind
2 Penn Plaza, Suite 1102
New York, NY 10121
Phone: 212-502-7600
Website: www.afb.org
Email: afbinfo@afb.net
Publishes a variety of books on visual
impairments, including *A Parent's Guide
to Special Education for Children with
Visual Impairments*

**American Printing House for
the Blind, Inc.**
1839 Frankfort Avenue
P.O. Box 6085
Louisville, KY 40206-0085
Phone: 800-223-1839; 502-895-2405
Website: www.aph.org
Email: info@aph.org
Manufactures educational aids for
blind and visually impaired persons,
has an educational research program,
sells books in braille, large print, disk
and cassette and offers a database for
locating textbooks and other materials in
accessible media

Bookshare
480 South California Avenue
Palo Alto, CA 94306
Phone: 650-352-0198
Website: www.bookshare.org
An accessible online library making the
world of print accessible to people with
disabilities

Learning Ally
20 Roszel Road
Princeton, NJ 08540
Phone: 800-221-4792
Website: www.learningally.org
Email: bvidialogue@LearningAlly.org
Produces accessible educational materials for students with visual impairments with titles available in every subject area and grade level from kindergarten through graduate studies

National Library Service for the Blind and Physically Handicapped: The Library of Congress
Phone: 800-424-8567; 202-707-5100
Website: www.loc.gov/nls
Email: nls@loc.gov
A free library program of braille and audio material circulated to eligible borrowers - an excellent resource for audio books for school-age children

Products for the Visually Impaired
The Lighthouse Guild Store (part of Lighthouse Guild)
15 West 65th Street
New York, NY 10023
Phone: 646-874-8384
Website: shop.lighthouseguild.org
Email: store@lighthouseguild.org
Offers a variety of products for the visually impaired including magnifiers, toys for children and computer accessories

LS & S
145 River Rock Drive
Buffalo, NY 14207
Phone: 800-468-4789
Website: www.lssproducts.com
Email: LSSInfo@LSSproducts.com
Provides a variety of products for those who are visually impaired

Toys and Games
Exceptional Teaching Inc.
P.O. Box 2330
Livermore, CA 94550
Phone: 800-549-6999
Website: www.exceptionalteaching.com
Email: info@exceptionalteaching.com
Offers toys and games for children with a visual impairment

Assistive Devices and Technology
AbleNet, Inc.
2625 Patton Road
Roseville, MN 55113-1308
Phone: 800-322-0956
Website: www.ablenetinc.com
Email: customerservice@ablenetinc.com
Offers a variety of adaptive keyboards with large buttons

Ai Squared
130 Taconic Business Park Road
Manchester Center, VT 05255
Phone: 802-362-3612
Website: www.aisquared.com
Offers ZoomText computer screen magnification and reading software for the visually impaired as well as large-print keyboards, ZoomText cameras and accessories

Freedom Scientific
11800 31st Court North
St. Petersburg, FL 33716
Phone: 800-444-4443; 727-803-8000
Website: www.freedomscientific.com
Offers a wide variety of low vision devices including desktop magnifiers, handheld video magnifiers and MAGic screen magnification software

Greystone Digital Inc.
P.O. Box 1888
Huntersville, NC 28078
Website: www.bigkeys.com
Email: sales@bigkeys.com
Sells Big Keys keyboards and other
adaptive devices

SightConnection
9709 Third Avenue, NE #100
Seattle, WA 98115
Phone: 800-458-4888; 206-525-5556
Website: www.sightconnection.com
Email: store@sightconnection.org
A not-for-profit organization that sells
magnifiers, CCTVs, keyboards and
other items adapted for visually impaired
people

Sun Safety Gear and Information
Baby Banz
205 A North Adams Avenue
Knob Noster, MO 65336
Phone: 877-333-0074
Website: www.banzworld.com
Email: info@babybanz.com
Provider of a variety of products including
sunglasses and sun-protective clothing

Coolibar
2401 Edgewood Avenue South
Suite 400
Minneapolis, MN 55426
Phone: 800-926-6509
Website: www.coolibar.com
Designs and manufactures a wide range
of sun-protection products that allow
people to safely enjoy outdoor activities
including sun-protective clothing,
sun hats, sun-protective swimwear,
sunglasses, umbrellas, sunscreens and
sunblock

Liberty Sport, Inc.
107 Fairfield Road
Fairfield, NJ 07004
Phone: 800-444-5010
Website: www.libertysport.com
A leading provider of prescription and
sports eyewear

NoIR Medical Technologies
6155 Pontiac Trail
South Lyon, MI 48178
Phone: 800-521-9746; 734-769-5565
Website: www.noir-medical.com
Email: noirsales@noirlaser.com
Specializing in low vision protective
eyewear for over 50 years

Solartex Sun Gear
10608 Purcell Road
Glen Allen, VA 23060
Phone: 877-476-5789
Website: www.solartex.com
Email: info@solartex.com
Provides a wide range of sun-protection
clothing, hats, sunglasses, sunscreen
and skin care products

SunGuard
Website: www.sunguardsunprotection.
com
Email: consumerservice@phoenixbrands.
com
Phone: 866-794-0800
A laundry aid that washes sun protection
into clothing and helps block more than
96% of the sun's UV rays - available
online

Sun Precautions
3809 9th Avenue South
Seattle, WA 98108
Phone: 800-882-7860
Website: www.sunprecautions.com
Manufactures Solumbra, a sun-
protection fabric, and provides a wide
range of apparel

Adaptive Sports and Camps
Adaptive Sports Association
P.O. Box 1884
Durango, CO 81302
Phone: 970-259-0374
Winter Program Office: 970-385-2163
Website: www.asadurango.com
Email: info@asadurango.com
Supports and transforms the lives of students who have physical and cognitive challenges through sports and recreation activities

Adaptive Sports Foundation
P.O. Box 266
100 Silverman Way
Windham, NY 12496
Phone: 518-734-5070
Website: www.adaptivesportsfoundation.org
Email: info@adaptivesportsfoundation.org
Offers both winter and summer sports clinics to a wide range of special needs children and adults

Camp Abilities PA@WCU
West Chester University of Pennsylvania
Phone: 610-436-2516
Website: www.campabilitiespa.org
Email: campabilitiespa@gmail.com
A developmental sports camp for children ages 7-17 who are blind or have low vision - search the Web for other Camp Abilities locations

Higher Ground Sun Valley (HG)
P.O. Box 6791
Ketchum, ID 83340
Phone: 208-726-9298
Website: www.highergroundsv.org
Email: info@HigherGroundSV.org
A nonprofit organization focused on enriching the lives of people with recreational activities and sports that works with 80 of the top adaptive sports programs in the country to provide high-quality adaptive sports programs that are safe, fun and have measurable outcomes

The National Beep Baseball Association
Phone: 866-400-4551
Website: www.nbba.org
Email: secretary@nbba.org
Provides information about beep baseball including registered teams and equipment for beep baseball

Space Camp for Interested Visually Impaired Students (SCIVIS)
Dan Oates - SCIVIS
190 Armstrong Street
Romney, WV 26757-1407
Phone: 304-851-5680
Website: www.tsbvi.edu/space
Email: scivis@atlanticbb.net
A week-long camp conducted by Teachers of the Visually Impaired where children can experience what it's like to train as an astronaut and prepare for a mission at the U.S. Space and Rocket Center in Alabama

United States Association of Blind Athletes
1 Olympic Plaza
Colorado Springs, CO 80909
Phone: 719-866-3224
Website: www.usaba.org
A member of the United States Olympic Committee, USABA offers training in a variety of sports for blind and low vision athletes

Sports Equipment
American Printing House for the Blind, Inc.
1839 Frankfort Avenue
P.O. Box 6085
Louisville, KY 40206-0085
Phone: 800-223-1839; 502-895-2405
Website: www.aph.org
Email: info@aph.org
Physical education equipment can be purchased from the APH store

CenturyLink Pioneers
100 CenturyLink Drive, 6th Floor
Monroe, LA 71201
Phone: 318-330-6454
Website: www.centurylinkpioneers.org
Email: beepball@qwestpioneers.org
In addition to beeping Easter eggs, manufactures and sells beep balls and accessories

Targe Innovations Inc.
9 Reuben Street
Suite 456
Kemptville ON K0G 1J0
Canada
Phone: 866-408-2743
Website: www.targeinnovations.com
Sells audible soccer balls and equipment for goalball, a team sport designed specifically for blind athletes

Special Interests
BaiChina
Website: http://groups.yahoo.com/groups/baichina
An online adoption support group for friends and family of children from China with albinism providing information people in the process of adopting a child with albinism from an Asian country and for families who have already adopted an Asian child with albinism

BiOptic Driving Network
Website: www.biopticdriving.org
Serves the needs and interests of those with stable low vision who may be able to drive with a miniaturized telescope

Positive Exposure
43 East 20th Street, 6th Floor
New York, NY 10003
Phone: 212-420-1931
Website: www.positiveexposure.org
Email: rick@positiveexposure.org
Conducts workshops and exhibitions for service providers, schools and the general public to challenge the stigma associated with physical difference using a very powerful tool to fight discrimination: evocative photographs representing persons of various ages and cultures with albinism

The Vision for Tomorrow Foundation
655 Deersfield Road
Suite 100 - #130
Deersfield, IL 60015-3241
Website: www.visionfortomorrow.org
Email: info@visionfortomorrow.org
Provides funding for research initiatives and offers support and information for those seeking to learn more about albinism and aniridia

The Vision of Children Foundation
12555 High Bluff Drive
Suite 330
San Diego, CA 92130
Phone: 858-314-7917
Website: www.visionofchildren.org
Email: info@visionofchildren.org
Advocates and supports research toward correcting conditions that cause vision impairment and blindness

Index

A Word About Positive Exposure and Rick Guidotti

Rick Guidotti, Director of Positive Exposure, completed his education in photography and filmmaking at New York's School of Visual Arts and established a studio in Manhattan, specializing in portraiture and fashion for 15 years.

As part of a personal and professional transformation, Rick in partnership with NOAH began the crusade to replace negative stereotypes of people living with albinism found in media and cinema. This new body of work celebrating the beauty of albinism was published in *Life* Magazine in 1998 in the article "Redefining Beauty" which won the Genetic Alliance's Art of Reporting Award.

In 1998, Rick founded Positive Exposure, a nonprofit organization that challenges stigma associated with difference by pioneering a new vision of the beauty and richness of genetic diversity. He has photographed people with albinism around the world, from Africa to the South Pacific, celebrating difference while educating health care workers, teachers, and community members about the challenges and unique beauty of those with the condition.

Currently Rick is leading Positive Exposure's initiatives within the health care community to connect students with the social realities of those living with genetic difference. Rick is currently the co-president of New York City's chapter of NOAH.

For more information please refer to **www.positiveexposure.org**.